reflecting
LEADERSHIP

*Leadership for building
a healthy society*

Editors
Sean Denyer, Leslie Boydell,
Jane Wilde and Una Hearne

Published by The Institute of Public Health in Ireland, 2003

ISBN 0-9542965-5-9

This book is not for sale for profit.

The Institute of Public Health

5th floor, Bishop's Square	Forestview
Redmond's Hill	Purdy's Lane
Dublin 2	Belfast BT8 7ZX
Ireland	Northern Ireland
Tel: 00 353 1 478 6300	Tel: 00 44 28 9064 8494
Fax: 00 353 1 478 6319	Fax: 00 44 28 9064 6604

Email: info@publichealth.ie   Website: www.publichealth.ie

Design and art direction by Artisan - www.artisan.ie

Image credits: pages 16, 20, 24, 42, 46, 52, 58, 64, 72, 74, 76, 88, 92, 96, 100, 104, 106, 118, 124, 128, 134, 136 Artisan; page 30 James Dodds *Interior of Hesper*, www.jamesdodds.co.uk; page 36 Nel Whatmore *Contata* detail, www.nelwhatmore.com; page 38 Stockbyte, page 56 Illustration Works, page 82 Photodisc, page 86 Getty Images; page 108 Robert Carr 'Untitled 1'; page 139 Photo of Gillie Bolton by Don McPhee, Guardian photographer.

This book is printed on Cyclus Offset 100% recycled paper

*Dedicated to everyone
who contributes to building
a healthy society*

Contents

Leadership in Action

Challenging Orthodoxies

Who we are

Acknowledgements

The Institute of Public Health would like to thank all those
who have contributed to the design and
delivery of our first leadership programme.
In particular we would like to acknowledge:

Anne McMurray (programme consultant),
Mike Kossler (Centre for Creative Leadership),
Thomas Rice and Marianne Hughes
(Interaction Institute for Social Change),
Gillie Bolton (reflective writing consultant),
Mhairi Cameron and Mike Dinham
(programme co-designers and tutors).

All those who attended the early workshops
to plan the programme.

The Advisory Group, Pat Donnelly (Chair),
Denis Doherty, David Bingham,
Carolyn Mason and Owen Metcalfe.

The Department of Health, Social Services
and Public Safety in Northern Ireland
and the Department of Health and Children
in Ireland who supported the programme.

Preface

This publication has been produced by the first group to take part in the leadership programme developed by the Institute of Public Health in Ireland. It reflects their learning and insights into themselves, the process of development they experienced and what they have achieved as a result. As the writings in this anthology convey, leadership involves increasing self-awareness, openness with others about what you really care about and a willingness to be honest about your vulnerabilities. The leaders who have compiled this collection have the courage to share with others offerings which will hopefully engage, inspire, move, entertain and educate you about your own leadership.

This programme was launched in January 2002 and the first group have now completed the programme. The programme consists of an initial briefing in January to meet one another and to agree a learning and support contract with each other and with the Institute. During the first year of the programme there are three modules lasting four to five days.

The first focuses on personal leadership development and is delivered by the Centre for Creative Leadership jointly with the programme consultant, Anne McMurray. The second module is concerned with systems, including tools to support change and an exploration of the 'shadow side', which can block change. The third module deals with leadership without executive authority and collaborative leadership. This includes an exercise in dialogue which is undertaken in a fishbowl format and is designed to explore a potentially volatile subject, in this case the role of an all-island leadership network for building a healthy society in post-conflict Northern Ireland. Two days on facilitative leadership are delivered by the Interaction Institute for Social

Change. During this module the participants are introduced to reflective writing by Gillie Bolton as a way of gaining further insight into their own leadership. This book is an expression of where this writing has been taken by the first group.

During the second year of the programme the focus is on taking forward an identified leadership challenge which each participant faces in their own area of work. This is something of strategic importance which can become a focus for the individual's leadership development. It also helps to demonstrate the impact of this programme. Participants meet formally about three times during the year for networking and to share progress. Many participants have also met informally to plan joint initiatives and offer mutual support.

The overall aim of the programme is, through successive programmes, to build a network of leaders from across the island of Ireland who will act creatively and collectively to build a healthier society. By the end of 2005, around 75 people will have been through this programme and will have had a common development experience, with a shared commitment to tackling inequalities in health and social injustice on this island. They work in public health, in health and social care organisations, in local councils, in government, in research bodies and in a range of voluntary and community organisations. They have the power to make a difference to the health and wellbeing of our population.

Leslie Boydell
Programme Director

'If we had to say what
writing is, we would
define it essentially
as an act of courage'

Cynthia Ozick

Introduction

The pieces in this book reflect on leadership and what it may be. They are personal and creative and not often what you would expect to see in a book on leadership. They demonstrate the importance to any leader of standing back, taking time out, and using creativity as an integral part of leadership.

The programme participants come from a wide range of sectors from all parts of the island of Ireland and this is reflected in some of the themes such as borders and boundaries and partnership working. The friendships and trust that developed between people on the programme provide a vision of what is possible.

'It is good to have
an end to journey towards;
but it is the journey
that matters in the end.'

Ursula le Guin

Personal journeys

The first collection of pieces concentrates on the personal journeys made by some of the participants in the programme. They highlight different aspects of the leadership programme and the effect it has had on their professional and personal lives.

Steering the leadership wagon

Leslie Boydell

'Leadership is working to understand the whole situation
and seeing to it that absolutely everything in it
goes well, without limit or reservation.'

Michael Simmons 1996

There are so many definitions of leadership, many of which
refer to shared leadership, distributed leadership, collaborative,
facilitative and so on. However, in my mind's eye, I still have a
view of the leader as up-front, out there, charismatic. I think
maybe this is quite a masculine image of leadership.

Leadership is an emotive concept. I like to think of myself as
a leader and not a follower. I suspect I am not alone in this
aspiration. And yet, when I compare myself with the image of
the visible leader I have just described, I feel daunted because
I am not sure I can ever be like that. As a strong introvert, it is
not just a step out of my comfort zone but a flying leap.

Then, during the third module of the programme, Anne, our
programme consultant, gave us the definition quoted at the
beginning of this piece and it resonated. I thought to myself,
YES!, this is the type of leader I can identify with.

I thought about the role I have taken in establishing this
programme. Essentially I started with a blank slate. I organised
workshops with public health leaders, attended conference
sessions on leadership, searched the Web, read papers, spoke to
people running programmes elsewhere and attended the Public
Health Leadership Institute in North Carolina in a team with

Carolyn Mason and Pat Donnelly. During this time I digested many ideas and was influenced by several people. The vision of what I wanted this programme to be formulated in my mind until it became something I wanted to fight for to bring to fruition. I have taken risks and overcome obstacles and many people have helped me. Some of those people have played a prominent role. But when I think back to that definition at the beginning, it fits. It is about understanding the big picture, seeing what is possible and appropriate and working to make sure that it goes really well, not just today but also tomorrow. For me that often meant getting the best people to carry forward various aspects of the programme that played to their strengths. My strengths are seeing the potential, finding the right people and giving them a chance to make it work as well as it possibly can, but I never take my eyes off it.

The most rewarding moments for me are when someone tells me that attending this programme has caused them to make a significant shift in their career or even in their life, and there have been a few. It also gives me great pleasure when someone who has been through the programme succeeds in making a major step in their career, such as a prestigious appointment to a strategic job. While we can't take all the credit for the leadership programme, it is particularly heartening when they acknowledge that it helped them to visualize themselves in that position. The other side of the coin is the angst I feel when someone is not satisfied with some aspect of the programme, and this has also happened. However, when I can give myself some distance from it, I always try to work out in consultation with them and with others, how we can learn from their experience to make sure it is better for those who follow them. Accepting that you can't please everyone all of the time is hard. I realised that during the short time I worked in general practice, when I discovered that one style of practice doesn't suit all patients. In a different way, it's the same lesson now.

As I thought about this, I asked myself what metaphor I would use for the programme. Almost immediately, the image that came to my mind was of a team of horses pulling a heavily laden wagon. The horses are of different sizes and colours and they are pulling at different speeds. One has the bit between its teeth and is going full tilt, another is taking it easy, a third wants to eat grass by the wayside, while another is grumpy and nipping the others. But every so often they pull together and we fly. I am sitting on the wagon, inconspicuous, without a whip or a loud voice. I constantly keep my eyes on the road ahead to steer around any dangers. Other people come on board for a while and ride with me and use their greater strength to control the horses and push them onwards.

So why the metaphor? Because metaphors help us to see things another way, from another perspective. We can develop them until they cease to be useful and then discard them. That's what is so delightful about them. You can play with them, unleash your and others' creative thinking and then move on, because at the end of the day the leadership programme is not a wagon and horses. It's a leadership programme.

Jigsaw

Cecilia Forrestal

Working across sectors, across disciplines, and across Ireland in a way that recognises the unique contribution that each one has to offer, the core differences between us and the desire to build upon what we have in common was for me the experience of the leadership programme.

Our common vision is for an equitable healthy Ireland. We share a belief in the wider definition of health and know that many aspects of how we organise society have to be different to make this vision a reality. How this can be achieved raises some of our differences, but equally highlights our unique contributions.

The programme encouraged us to stay focussed on what we have in common and through dialogue to explore how our differences could be exploited constructively to maximise our individual and collective contributions.

This sounds so simple, but it is worth noting how hard it is to sit with difference. We are more accustomed to spotting difference and taking up a position in opposition to it. We rush to solutions and to operational mode. We rush to what is familiar, even though we know that the familiar has not worked.

Staying with difference is uncomfortable. It raises feelings of loyalty to old ways of being, ways that are hard to let go of. It exposes us to the fear of uncertainty and new directions in routes where we have no tracks to follow. It challenges us to trust, when sometimes our past experiences have taught us to be cautious. It invites us to change and change is so difficult.

My belief about leadership is that it is strong when it is accompanied by vulnerability. Inner vulnerability, when expressed in an atmosphere that is non-judgmental, that is comfortable with uncertainty and that seeks the common good allows the core of a person to be seen and felt by the other. This experience of honesty is the way forward in terms of building collaborative working relationships across difference.

'It takes time to save time.' The programme gave time, a commodity we seldom have, to exploring honest leadership.

Like a piece in a jigsaw puzzle, I have been in my box for a long time. The other pieces are all around me. Some I can see and some I know by shape, others by the edges of their boundaries and others again by their colours. While the box has been shaken and moved at different times in the past, we have never really moved places to any great extent. I have found a way of being here in harmony of sorts, knowing my place and mindful of those around me.

The box is moving! The lid is opening! Oh the light! It stings my eyes. Something is happening. Someone is turning the pieces out onto the table and facing them all upright. My God. There are more pieces here than I was aware of. And look at the colours and shapes.

I feel vulnerable and lost. I have significantly moved from my comfortable corner. I am among others I have never met before. What is happening? Where will I fit in? Does anyone know the picture we are supposed to make?

Well, look at that! I thought that blue piece was definitely part of the sky. But No. It is water. And that piece of 'cloud' is part of the snow! Who would have guessed I could be so wrong? Now I can see the value of that sharp edge – you would have to have it in order to put shape on the whole picture.

This is exciting. I can see where I connect in. My unique colour and shape is necessary too. In fact, every piece is essential.

Leave me here a while in my new position. Allow me time to readjust my way of seeing and understanding it all. Give me space to see you differently and to appreciate how you fit in from this new angle. And, in time, I will be ready to be supported, to be moved, to be broken up again, to be the first out of the box, to be reformed, to be displayed, happy in the knowledge that the finished picture is greater than the parts.

What I'm not
(can an insider be an 'other'?)

Carolyn Mason

Northern Ireland is a place of either/or: Protestant or Catholic, British or Irish, loyalist or republican. It can be Ulster, Northern Ireland, the North of Ireland, or Ireland, depending on where you are coming from.

Under equality legislation we are asked if we have a 'perceived identity' as Protestant or Catholic or other. Because I went to a state school in Northern Ireland, largely Protestant, this is what I should probably put, in the spirit of the question. But it feels so wrong, so sectarian, that I write in 'other'.

> I'm not Irish
> But I'm not quite British
> I'm not really 'other'
> So what am I?
>
> The no identity people…
>
> If we can't say
> Who we are
> What we are, or
> Where we live
> Then how can we say what we want?

'What was it like to be in the Troubles?'

Carolyn Mason

Sudden exposure

Fear, beating and beating and beating.

Everyone watching – is the air thicker? It feels damp.
We just don't

Talk about these things.

Why is this person pursuing, insisting, closing in,
his intellectual curiosity

Slicing into the raw fear, anger, bloodied memories,

The purposely forgotten.

Why is he hunting, what is he touching?

Why am I so afraid?

Why should *I* tell the whole world? This is *my*

Deep, and my dark, why should I go back down in there,
in front of all these people?

I don't even know what I'm going back into, it's

Dark, and it's past. It's a

Feeling, and not a word.

Beside me, Eleanor feels safe – she's been there

She's crumpling, so we'll be blanketed together
and cover it up, and

Take away your spotlight, move it over

It's our sore, not your spectacle,

So move over gently

We'll pull the blanket softly over, and let's move on to the

Safety of our thinking, our words, our

Masks and our poise, our

Humour and our clever.

We can show, we can play, we can perform,

Exposed in the safety of our privacy.

This came out of an exercise called the goldfish bowl, where an inner circle of people discussed a topic, watched by an outer circle of people who would then comment on our performance.

The difficult question

Sean Denyer

We sit in a circle,
Inside a circle,
Like fish in a bowl
Being observed.

The topic is the Troubles.
We skirt around it,
Carefully, delicately,
Like skaters on very thin ice.

I look at Ruth, my observer,
Her bright eyes give me courage,
They say, 'go for it!'

I pause, heart pounding, mouth dry,
And say,
'What was it like to be in the Troubles?' It's out there.
Unleashed, alive, baring sharp, powerful teeth
Ready to bite.

You look stunned,
Like a deer,
Caught in the headlights,
The moment before the truck hits.

Was I right to ask?
To name it so nakedly,
Without a protective veil.

It came at some cost.
To me as well as you.
But perhaps at a price worth paying.

So I ask myself now,
How much more do we pay
For dodging the difficult question?

If leaders are born,
I was not one of them

Ruth Sutherland

If leaders are born, I was not one of them. A lifetime of caring, conciliation and compromise, of facilitation, mediation and pleasing people, did not promise to be the qualities of a public health leader.

Did the programme make me a leader? No, for neither are leaders made, but the experience for me has been an empowering one. For I have come to own the idea that not only have I been a leader, but that there is great potential to develop this role. I have come to appreciate that the attributes for public health leadership are many. I have had the opportunity to understand that maybe the skills required to engage the often inaudible voices of those who are most vulnerable to poor health and who are the biggest net losers in the near silent public health debate, are the qualities that lie at the heart of relationship building.

This opportunity in professional development is all too rare in the community and voluntary sector, and was made available to me through a public sector bursary. I most appreciated the space, maybe the permission, at a midway point in a demanding career juggled with heavy family commitments, to reflect upon and analyse in a supportive environment the role I play and the skills I use and need. Where I started with the appreciation of the luxury of this opportunity I have concluded with the belief that time for professional development is a necessity, a right, not just an associated benefit of privilege.

Overall, the experience has confirmed for me the significance and the potential of the link between community development and health as a powerful force for change, particularly in the face of the challenge of inequalities in health and those marginalised by them.

If public health is both an art and a science, then community development is part of the art. The art involved in understanding and nurturing the elements of social capital, of bridging and bonding. Social cohesion is the potential liquid gold elixir that we are beginning to understand plays a unique role in making and keeping us healthy. This is the kind of social protection that some, through the good fortune of life's lottery, are cradled with from birth, whilst others are consigned to early graves for the lack of it.

Considering the many styles of leadership I found the common traits to be commitment, passion and vision. In my experience it is the drive towards a vision that brings out the qualities of leadership, even in the reluctant.

There is ample pressure to catalyse leadership, to be committed, passionate and visionary in the field of public health in Ireland. The vast loss and limiting of life from preventable causes. The unacceptable and widening inequalities that make the difference in length of life between rich and poor, amongst the constructed divisions in society, as much as eight years. Also, and perhaps more significantly, that towards the end of already shorter lives the disadvantaged will experience considerably longer periods of chronic illness, as much as 13 years more than their advantaged counterparts.

Working in and alongside disadvantaged and marginalised groups brings a reality to the academic. The reality that contains such spectres as a young woman trying to sell the batteries from her radio in order to buy the next cigarette and nappy which are conveniently sold in individual packs of one cigarette and one nappy at the corner shop.

For inspiration, and as a prime example of leadership of change with apparently no power, we need to look no further than another young woman, Mrs Rosa Parks. Her quiet but defiant act of sitting in the whites-only section of a Montgomery (USA) bus in 1956 fuelled a civil rights movement. To quote Baroness Blood, the tireless Belfast community leader: 'Courage is like a muscle, the more you use it, the bigger it gets'.

The daily business of community development provides us with a wealth of examples of individuals and groups who make a difference, who identify problems and collaborate to work for change.

We can look to the great feats of history for inspiration. At the heart of human achievement is the necessity of cooperation and collaboration. Of the many examples I choose the inspiration of the earliest boat builders and explorers (see image). The boat is made up of the collaboration of each of the parts which make it seaworthy – one small piece astray will spell disaster. The skill and experience of the boat builder must craft the wood into the shape of the bow. It cannot be forced but must be nurtured into place. The image has further resonance when considering the courage and tenacity of the earliest explorers, who set forth upon uncharted waters bound for unknown destinations, carried only by the belief that the collaboration (the boat) would hold strong and their collaboration with each other and the elements (wind, sea and stars) would bring them back.

The public health movement could be considerably strengthened if the passion, commitment and vision of people, their communities and organisations could be understood, valued and collaborated with.

One small cameo of experience early on in the programme provided an invaluable insight. It resulted from a peer observation and feedback exercise. My study group analysis of a video of ourselves undertaking a task revealed the observation of me acquiescing to the group, even though it became obvious that I had identified and offered first the solution that the group eventually reached. The video revealed me sitting back and waiting for the group to come to the same conclusion. Above the table at which the group was sitting my body language and whole demeanour was open and facilitative. Yet under the table, my legs and feet betrayed a furious agitation of the frustration and annoyance that the group was being slow and not accepting of the solution offered. This valuable insight somehow encapsulated much of the paradox I often find myself in. It has taught me to be more economical with some of the qualities I possess and to liberate others.

The leadership programme affirmed for me the importance of emphasising strengths and curbing wasted activity. It energised me to appreciate the ignition that drives leadership. For me this is the quest for social justice that could result in health for all.

However, whilst highlighting the potential for leadership, the experience also tormented me with the paradox of the reality of existence. My daily grind in the community and voluntary sector, drowning in organisational necessities and all the bureaucracies one must deal with. This is the shaky foundation upon which bold leadership strives to build. The reality includes the need to raise one's own and others' salaries before the luxury of leadership can proceed. And also the apparent impossibility of carving out a legitimate niche, within the traditional world of public health, from which to mobilise the potential of the public to contribute to their health and that of their communities.

For many, reconciling the paradox means moving to new roles, into the ether of policy, strategy and/or academia, a welcoming and fitting place for creative, strategic visionaries. However, faced with the choices that the programme afforded, I concluded that statistics, research and policy development, however stimulating, interesting and necessary for change, do not serve to ignite, develop or sustain the passion and drive for change, in quite the same way as people do, for me. How they define themselves, how they relate and adjust to each other and the circumstances in which they find themselves, how they work together to identify and achieve common goals.

The privilege of being the witness or the midwife to physical, personal, social and political growth is something that working in the community and voluntary sector can offer, and is possibly of more solace in old age than a pension!

So the outcome of the dilemma raised by the programme for me has been to aim to get on top of the organisational and bureaucratic burdens – to acquire more motivation, skills and resources in these areas (contrary to the forecast of my Myers Briggs astrology). I would like to develop and sustain a functioning, efficient and effective machinery that rewards its leader with sufficient opportunity for creative playtime. So that ultimately the existence of all the work of the organisation, leadership, facilitation, support and networking will play a crucial role in public health.

Look through the window

Jane Wilde

There is a small town in the centre of Spain, near Seville, called Carmona. And in its winding back streets is a museum. It's a real treasure. What caught my eye was a small white exhibit, about four foot by four foot, like a miniature Moorish building. It had small square windows, each the colour of a jewel; turquoise, emerald, ruby, amethyst. They reminded me of spangles. I bent down to look more closely. A light shone in each of the squares, and lit up in each a scene, an illuminated picture, reflecting and portraying a picture of the past.

A way of holding on to memories, I thought, of past times, of revisiting scenes which might be forgotten.

The card opposite reminded me of those windows.

I think of events in the leadership programme as pictures in these windows. Looking back they seem like excerpts, events to be savoured, sweet or bittersweet, events that hold a particular meaning.

My leadership year

Catherine Hazlett

Owen Metcalfe invited me to join the Institute of Public Health. Leadership Programme at the end of 2001. He explained that the programme was a new initiative – the first of its kind in the public health and social services fields in Ireland at that time. The goal was to grow and develop advocates for people's health and wellbeing. The programme was to be run on an all–island basis with an equal number of participants drawn from North and South. I was delighted to be asked to join. I knew this was a unique opportunity. I was concerned about the time commitment involved and somewhat apprehensive about the possibility that participants would be mostly drawn from the health services. With a small degree of caution I signed up for the programme.

Our first get together was in Dublin in January 2002. The Minister for Children formally launched the programme at a reception followed by dinner. I knew only one or two participants to start with, but there were others in the same predicament. By the end of the evening having been 'moved' to a different table after every course, missing out on desert as a result, I certainly felt included and that we had started to get to know each other.

The first module was in the beautiful Radisson Roe Hotel in Limavady. We were introduced to our group members and we started to build the relationships which were to become so important to each of us as we embarked on the exploration of different leadership styles. And what a week it was to be. I immersed myself in self-scrutiny of my style and the impact of my behaviour on others. I learned to recognise the effect of different behaviours on myself and to look beyond what was outwardly observable in others. I learned to appreciate the wonderful diversity of people's behaviours and what fun it can be to understand the dynamics and the potential synergies of human relationships in the workplace. It is all about risk-taking we were told. And what risks there were! How can I ever forget the blizzard survival test, outdoor team building games, the hoops, the eggs, falling out of trees and miraculously being caught?

Myers Briggs, Firo B, 360° By Design... all brought new insights, which were at times reassuring, and sometimes discomfiting. Our group shared some of our innermost thoughts and aspirations and our doubts about what we wanted to achieve in our jobs and in public service. Together we experienced the feelings of exposure, and the vulnerability which goes with the territory. Many of us had our first experience of the benefits to be gained from executive coaching.

There were welcome breaks when we could enjoy the beautiful surroundings and take long walks in the countryside. With trepidation we dressed for dinner one night to hear style guru Billy Dickson give us advice and guidance on dressing the part.

Our summer module was in Inchydoney in Cork. It was another intensive week. This time we were presented with the tools and techniques every leader needs. We explored the dynamics of power in relationships, how systems are constructed and the processes that need to work effectively in bringing about change. The theory was hard work but it was practical and useful. Leading systems change, the shadow side of organisations, the complex and difficult theory of constraints – a veritable tool box for every eventuality. We were encouraged to take care of ourselves. We had opportunities to relax, take exercise, and explore what tai-chi and meditation might offer, the lesson being that each dimension of our lives is equally important. Lots of resolutions were made.

The final part of the programme, the third module, followed the same pace. Once again we had a beautiful venue in Tullamore but a very full schedule and not a lot of time for relaxation. By then we could look forward to the familiarity of our now cohesive and comforting groups. We continued to explore the mechanisms and processes for getting to the root of problems and building shared ownership of solutions. This time we tackled thorny matters such as how to exert influence without executive authority, and we tried out techniques for creating an environment for collaborative leadership. Then came the big push. 'Articulating a vision and inspiring others to follow' was for me the most challenging part of the programme. I felt the self-doubt, the embarrassment and the exhilaration in taking this giant step. I learned to appreciate the courage it takes to seek this very public affirmation of the leadership role.

Throughout the programme we were encouraged to keep a journal to record important events, assess their impact on ourselves and on others and to record our personal reflections on the issues that might shape our leadership development.

Shortly after we finished the formal part of the programme things changed in my work life and the prospect of a new career path opened up unexpectedly. I took on board the change. I found it difficult at times and personally demanding but all in all it has been an enriching experience. During this time and indeed since I have started to develop my new job, much of what I have learned on the programme has been of real assistance to me. Confronting and leading change are part and parcel of all our responsibilities as public service reform gathers pace. My experience on the programme has served me well. I continue to draw on the lessons learned. My journal has become a valuable source of wisdom for me and with practice I have found that several of the tools and techniques really do work.

I have continued to draw on the support of my fellow leaders who shared the experience with me. Some of them have been called upon to assume leadership roles in a very public way. Time and again as I see them in action I am reminded of the personal mastery, inner resourcefulness and deep commitment to public service that was so very evident during my leadership year. These are the experiences that will stay with me and from which I will continue to draw inspiration as I chart my course in the years ahead.

Vietnam on Saturday. Monday in Limavady

Jane Wilde

I left Ireland in sleet and snow and came back in spring.
I'd been to Vietnam and the contrast could not have been sharper.
I came back to the start of the leadership programme and felt
disequilibrium. I wrote this to express my need to reflect.

Vietnam on Saturday. Monday in Limavady.

The first day of the Leadership Programme:

Jump. Catch. Move over.

What do others think of you?

People everywhere: groups, teams, circles.

Who are you?

Your lifeline? Your story? Your feedback?

Who are you?

The clean green smell of May in Ireland

Lush green grass sparkles with last night's rain

The morning light is bright and clear

A lark sings unashamedly in the clear blue morning sky

Later walking along the river bank
I slip on the narrow stony path
Damp from the soft mizzly afternoon rain
Dripping on the back of curved grass

The stones in the river are dull and grey
The sky low and gloomy lies on my shoulders
And clouds are in my head
A heron balances on a stone in the river

We watched and waited for each other
He held my gaze. Balanced
Silent, still, surveying
Later, gently with ease, he flew

A journey in leadership

John McMullen

In The Beginning

The invitation to form part of an all–Ireland working group to explore the feasibility of a training programme for public health leaders came as a surprise. To this day I do not know what triggered the suggestion, but the opportunity was both exciting and challenging. The process of interacting with professionals from cross–sectoral backgrounds established, without any doubt, a clear necessity for such an initiative. The suggestion that I could and should participate in the first programme was initially flattering, but given the considerable time commitment necessary, required me to think in more detail of the implications. That process of reflection led me for the first time in many years to look at 'me' and my needs, which contrasted starkly with my regular preoccupation of looking at the needs of my staff. I realised that I had not thought of 'me' for a long time, particularly not as a leader, nor indeed my personal development needs, and the potential advantages for me personally, my work and the organisation's development.

In reality it took very little to hook me on the idea. However, I am certain that I approached my participation with a considerable degree of naivety in respect of both the challenge and opportunity for growth that the programme was to present me with. I hope in this short article to reflect on some of the highlights of the leadership programme, which to this day, remains for me a meaningful and challenging experience.

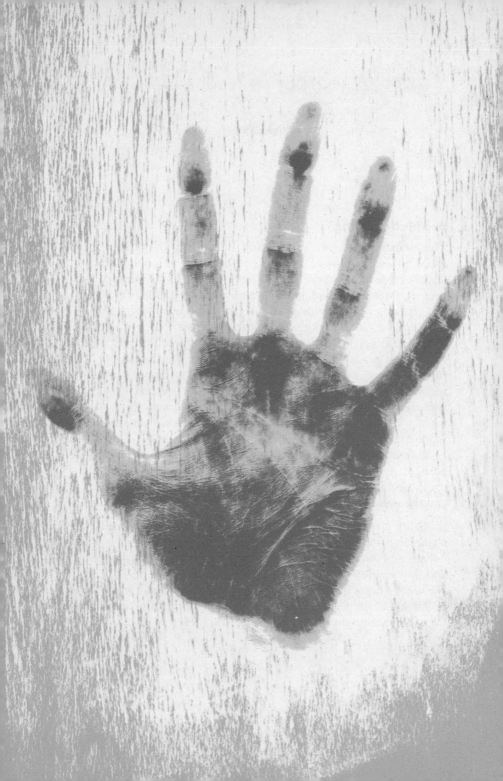

Learning About Me

I remember clearly that one of the first tasks during our initial residential was to develop a timeline telling your personal story and critical life events using key words and hand-drawn graphics. In particular, this activity and the quality of the artwork served to confirm how little I deserved the 'A' level qualification in art that I had aquired so many years ago. Nevertheless, presenting my experiences, sharing with others and responding to their questions set the scene for the remainder of the programme and underlined the amount of emotional capital which would have to be invested to benefit from the leadership programme. I personally found that in the early parts of the programme, the focus on self and third party assessment to be invaluable.

The programme provided me with both the opportunity and tools to help me explore and understand myself. In particular, the Myers Briggs assessment confirmed me as a very proud ENFJ, but more importantly it taught me about my personality profile, specifically that it was neither good nor bad, nor right nor wrong. To put it simply, ENFJ is just 'me' and it reflects the way I like to do things. It told me that I have strong ideals on how organisations should treat people and that I like to facilitate teams and encourage cooperation. I like to lead through personal enthusiasm and praise. I have a participative approach to management. I learn through interaction and cooperation. I problem solve by considering the impacts which are based on factual data. I encourage self-expression and have a person focus, while providing encouragement, support and appreciation. There you are, that's me sorted, I am clearly a good guy! More importantly, from a leadership perspective, by understanding 'me', I know my strengths and importantly my weaknesses, my preferences and my dislikes and all these combine to help me do what I have to do, better.

The next formidable challenge provided by the programme was the benignly titled 360° performance review. Now that was a worrying experience, asking your boss, your peers and subordinates (I hate that word subordinate, but then I am an ENFJ) to record what they think of you, while at the same time, and more worryingly, offering them complete anonymity. I must record that I found the process more rewarding than challenging and confirmed to me my own personally acknowledged weakness ie, I might listen to what people are saying, but I do not always hear, as I have usually already decided the best response to a particular issue. The process did not teach me to change (after all, when it does go wrong I get it in the neck), but it did encourage me to ensure that I tell people that what they say is very valuable and to explain, if necessary, why I intend to act in another way. But the tool is a powerful aid and helped considerably in my journey through leadership.

Working With Others

The learning support groups/sets, which were put in place from day one of the programme, were a tremendous resource. The building of close working relationships with peers to depend on and seek support from was invaluable. I still recall, with considerable trepidation, the first time that my learning group went into closed session to frankly, critically and collectively review each individual's performance and contribution throughout the programme. Describing it as a moment which was emotionally charged fails to capture the experience. Upon reflection, I think the moment the feedback began created in me a sense of emotional nudity, but the depth of trust, strength of bond and the friendship achieved as a result, lasted throughout the programme, supported the learning and, I believe, will continue to last into the future.

Being honest, I must admit that I really enjoyed the opportunities to develop and practice coaching skills. Coaching comes naturally to me, but what else would you expect, I am an ENFJ after all. I vividly remember a wet afternoon in Limavady when challenged by a series of physical tasks, that I for the first time came to understand the total lack of physical coordination which appeared to be endemic within the health professional network on this island. One other thing I learnt from the exercise was that while my public health colleagues are undoubtedly expert and much experienced in their own fields, they must not under any circumstances ever be trusted with the safe transport of half-a-dozen raw eggs. While to many that might be a simple task, it clearly has a complexity all of its own which was demonstrably beyond our collective competence.

Organisational Development

This journey in leadership moved us beyond personal introspection and assisted us in looking at our role and interaction as leaders in the context of our organisations. We looked at the impact of a facilitative approach to leadership within our organisations and structures. We looked at tapping into the power of participation, we developed and tested a tool kit and reflected upon its application within our own organisational structures. We examined approaches to decision-making, and in particular structured approaches. We investigated the concept of clouds (and it sometimes appeared that this was where our heads were). We examined from our own experience the two Ps (Politics and Power) and engaged in looking at the 'shadow side' in organisations. It was helpful to think of this concept in terms of real experiences and the understanding that if managed effectively, the naturally occurring 'shadow side' can be a force for positive effect and development.

And Finally

The programme has provided me with a performance challenge and considerable personal growth. I know I have grown in confidence because I understand myself better. I have been able to benchmark myself with peers, while developing along with them. I suspect that I have become more challenging to the individuals and bodies with which I do not agree, but part of this journey has been building confidence to become more assertive while developing and deploying the range of tools and techniques acquired through the programme.

There were, however, two surprising consequences resulting from my participation in the programme. The first of these I only acknowledged through the process of reflective writing which we all engaged in. It occurred to me that when trying to put on paper actual examples of the impact the programme had on me, I became aware that I had begun, unconsciously, to redecorate my office space. I honestly had not been aware that I was acquiring paintings, furniture and ornaments, and had fully redecorated my office. I think that this subconscious activity was me highlighting that the journey had taken me through to a place of confidence and allowed me to acknowledge that I am good at what I do and that I didn't get my job by default but have earned it.

The second and more disconcerting experience, at least for my long-suffering wife, Tina, was as a result of being 'style-gurued' by Billy Dickson. I have taken a greater interest in how I dress and can now comment, with some authority, on colour coordination, cut of suits and colours of shirts, where before I had to rely on others for advice. I think this caused Tina to question what I was actually doing during those week-long residentials away from home.

However, I can finish this short article with the certainty that my experience has been invaluable to me personally and to my organisation and I know that the many other participants who will travel this road will undoubtedly have an equally rewarding experience.

I am enough!

Eleanor Gill

What a return on investment! The leadership programme has helped me to get to know me better. I am tuned in to me, which helps me to tune in to others.

I have exorcised those ghosts, quelled those inner, doubting voices silently shouting within me. I have nothing to prove to myself or others.

I am blessed – I AM ENOUGH!

Thank you.

'Leadership is both active and reflective. One has to alternate between participating and observing.'

Ronald Heifetz

Leadership in action

The next set of pieces explore leadership in action. Programme participants from varying backgrounds give real life examples of bringing about change through processes which reflect learning gained through the programme.

Making a difference!

Liz Keane

November morning. Patrick's Bridge. Biting cold. Menacing dark clouds gathering behind Shandon and the Northside. Sleety rain. Torrents of muddy water splashing in the gutters. There he was. A crouched figure in torn, dirty, ragged clothes.
An empty whiskey bottle in his gnarled, nicotine-stained hands. What a shame! What a tragedy! Thought to myself – what would his mother say if she saw him now? Yes, he must have had a mother. A mother who gave birth to a beautiful baby boy.
A baby equal to all other baby boys born in that hospital that day. What went wrong? Why him? Is he to blame? Is society to blame Who or what can put it right? Who can make a difference?

Simple questions to ask, maybe. But oh so complex to answer. We could treat him – bring him to Accident and Emergency or maybe to the Simon Hostel. Is that helping him or merely removing him from our vision, from our bridge?

Maybe we should change the alcohol laws? Prohibition. Increasing cost. Harder to come by. Yes, but dependency rules. Oh to be so helpless!

Yet we can't stand idly by. I can't stand idly by. I must rise to the challenge. The leadership challenge. Must make a difference.

Fuel poverty, a tipping point: lessons in community action

John Briggs

It is 20 January 1999 and Jack is patiently lying in his bed waiting for his son to arrive and light the fire in the living room. He plans to get up in time to see the lunchtime news and to enjoy his dinner in front of the blazing fire his son will prepare.

First he has to leave his warm bed and step into the cold air of the bedroom. He needs a Zimmer frame to move around now because of his back problem. Jack's morning time in the bathroom is kept to a minimum, no heat, severe condensation and a room cluttered with disability aids is not very inviting. He loves the feeling of finally being able to settle down in his armchair in front of the fire. And there he stays – a prisoner of the cold.

Jack is in his early seventies and has always lived a rural life. He has served his generation well and now in his retirement he is happy to accept his lot, the regular visits to his doctor, his back pain, drugs etc, but he doesn't like handouts. He likes to remain independent but the fact is that he is very dependent upon his sons and neighbours to keep him warm during the long winter months.

In the same month, Eleanor has taken up her post as Health Action Zone Manager. She is fit and well and in contrast to Jack is sitting in her centrally-heated office mulling over the various documents, circulars and letters which have been sent to her for possible action. Her partners across the different organisations such as councils, Housing Executive and community organisations have identified housing and health as a key theme for action.

One letter sent to her by the Director of Public Health catches her eye. It was a request from the Housing Executive to set up a scheme to provide warm energy efficient homes for vulnerable households. It was a request for funding, but the Health Action Zone had no available resources. The letter had 'bin potential' written all over it, but something made Eleanor take it further. A gut feeling, a vision of people enjoying warm, dry homes as a right, a means of making a difference.

Over the next three months Eleanor made connections. She visited all interested and some not interested parties. She brought together people from different professional and community backgrounds. She learnt more about how a scheme would work but she was also told how the scheme would fail, how certain sections of the community would not accept handouts and how so many schemes never reach their full potential.

One particular connection, however, kept Eleanor focusing on her vision. A visit to Noel in the Housing Executive gave her the hard facts, the statistics, the indepth knowledge of how this scheme would work and the impact it could have. Noel didn't just have the information at his fingertips, he kept it in his head and he loved giving it away. He believed he was given the information to give away. He was a real database of hard facts on the whys and wherefores of Fuel Poverty.

As Eleanor considered the future she knew that she needed a real salesperson to sell the scheme, someone who would become immersed in the community, someone who would be persistent, who would speak the same language, who would understand the culture of strong independent people who didn't want handouts, and someone who just loved selling the scheme.

By June 2000 funding had been achieved and a full partnership put together. Interviews took place for a Community Energy Advisor and in walked Joan. The interview panel straight away knew they had the right person. Her background was in energy efficiency, but it was her nature, her ability to interact at a local level which made sure Joan got the job.

In September 2000 the 'Home Is Where The Heat Is' scheme got underway. The team had analysed the situation. They needed a 'stickiness factor' to make sure the scheme was a success. It was decided that the scheme needed to be owned and trusted by the community, and the individuals living within it, if it was to meet its optimum potential. People trust the idea more if it looks like it's catching on – people like Jack. Time and space would be provided to sell the idea. Joan worked tirelessly in the community. She spoke to groups, to individuals, she attended community Christmas dinners, she listened and became friends with everyone she met – she was accepted as a trusted part of the community.

By September 2001 the scheme had 'tipped', it had become a resounding success: 100% take-up of funds, households changed for the better. The vision, the connections, the information and the promotion by the few had made a difference.

It is my belief that the public health leadership network can learn from such experiences in order to make a real difference for local communities and people. Malcolm Gladwell in his book *The Tipping Point* sets out key factors in turning routine issues into an epidemic or a good idea into a phenomenon – they have such resonance for public health leaders.

He argues that you need 'connectors' to act as the social glue, to have their foot in many camps and to bring people together towards a common vision. When people are brought together they need information fuel to drive the engine of the vision. Gladwell calls these people 'mavens'. They are people who not only absorb the relevant information but they give it away so readily. 'Salesmen' are also needed to actually persuade people to change, to take part. When you have these people acting together, Gladwell claims a situation can 'tip'.

Two other factors are also stressed in his book. Research indicates that a 'stickiness factor' is necessary to 'tip' a routine incident into an epidemic, a factor that won't shake off, that won't go away, that makes a difference. Sometimes the 'stickiness factor' can appear trivial to people outside the issue or sometimes it is so obvious that it is missed because no-one has taken responsibility for ensuring it is progressed. The other key factor that Gladwell argues is important to consider is the environment in which the action is occurring. It is vitally important that the environment and the issue are complementary. This factor again seems so obvious but on many occasions successful health schemes are transferred to new locations, new communities and new environments without due consideration of the local circumstances.

The fuel poverty scheme got it right. The scheme was designed to match the local environment and indeed the 'stickiness factor' was identified at an early stage as the commitment to ensuring ownership by and generating trust in the local community.

The right people were in place: the connectors, the mavens and the salesmen. The ingredients were well mixed and the scheme tipped.

Jack is now able to get up when he wants in the winter time. He is not dependent upon his son anymore. His house is fully centrally heated and he loves it. His bathroom is now warm and there is hot water on tap. There are no clumsy aids needed anymore because his back pain has improved immensely. His drugs have reduced and he even gets out and about more in his car. He has a new lease of life.

Health research and the coordination of National Research Policy

Ruth Barrington

During the public health leadership programme I was faced with one of the major challenges of my career – to represent the interests of health research as a member of a commission established by the Minister for Enterprise, Trade and Employment to report on a national system to coordinate research.

There was agreement that national coordination of research activities was needed. Under the National Development Plan, the Higher Education Authority was funding a major investment programme in research infrastructure in third level colleges (PRTLI). Two new research funding councils were established to support research in science and technology and the humanities and social sciences. Science Foundation Ireland, established by the Minister for Enterprise, Trade and Employment in 2001, was making unprecedented levels of funding available by competition for research linked to economic development. The budget of my organisation, the Health Research Board (HRB), had quadrupled since 1998 and with the publication of *Making Knowledge Work for Health – A Strategy for Health Research* in 2001, the Minister for Health and Children had indicated the strategic importance of research to his department.

The question was what was meant by 'national coordination' of research. The suddenness of the change in the climate of research and the appearance of new research funding bodies led to criticisms that there was 'overlap and duplication' and that research support should be 'simplified'. Some suggested that all funding for research should come from one body and that

funding should be clearly linked to economic objectives. Others argued that Ireland was simply catching up with countries with mature research systems, in which it was recognised that support for research served a number of different but equally legitimate functions, such as high quality teaching, building intellectual capital, enhanced patient care and economic development and that there should be a variety of support available to reflect these different goals. The challenge for this school of thought was not so much to reduce the number of funding bodies but to ensure that research policy across all government agencies was coherent and complementary. The HRB was strongly in favour of this latter approach.

There were difficulties from the moment the commission was announced in April 2002. The task of establishing and chairing the commission was delegated to the Chair of the Irish Council for Science, Technology and Innovation (ICSTI), an advisory body to the Department of Enterprise, Trade and Employment (DETE), which was an unusual way of establishing a commission. It appeared that initially all the members of the commission would be experts from abroad or persons from the DETE 'family' of agencies. Alarm bells rang in the Departments of Health and Children and Education and Science, two departments with significant research responsibilities, that such a membership would predispose the commission to recommend that all research be coordinated (and possibly funded) by DETE or its associated bodies. A 'behind the scenes' campaign began to ensure that the interests of both departments and their research funding bodies were represented on the commission. I was informed that the Minister for Health wished to nominate me to the commission.

The second module of the Public Health Leadership course took place some weeks before the first meeting of the commission. I was aware that a difficult assignment lay ahead. I had been energised by the first module of the course to deal with a difficult issue in my organisation and to change aspects of my style of management and had been pleased with how well things had gone. It had done great things for my self confidence. But membership of the commission posed a challenge of a different order. During the second module, I used the problem of the commission to test the theory of constraints and presented the challenge of the commission to colleagues in small group sessions for their insight and advice. The module helped me to see clearly that my role on the commission would be to protect the identity of health research within a national system of research coordination. To do this, I needed to look at models that worked in other countries and to draft a good submission that would have the support of the board members, that would give me a mandate on the commission and that would hopefully influence thinking by other organisations involved in the process.

On return to the office, I commissioned some consultancy work on the organisation of health research in other countries and began drafting the HRB submission. I was informed of my membership the day before the first meeting of the commission on 19 June. The number of nominees of the Minister of Education and Science had not been resolved by the first meeting and only one representative attended.

The first meeting of the commission was preceded by a dinner on 18 June in a south Dublin hotel in a room ominously named 'Lepanto'. The Chair and representatives of the DETE explained, for the benefit of the overseas members (of which there were five) the background to the establishment of the commission. However, no mention was made of the difficulties the establishment of the commission had caused nor the unresolved issue of membership. I felt that it was necessary to explain to the overseas members that there were difficulties about the establishment of the commission and that these had not yet been resolved. I don't think any intervention I ever made before had such an impact on the group to which it was addressed. I was supported by the nominee of the Minister for Education and Science who pointed out that he was attending the dinner and first meeting 'without prejudice' to the issue of the final representation from the education sector on the commission. A tense discussion ensued with one overseas member commenting that he could see 'an elephant' on the table.

We assembled next day for the first meeting. It was clear from the beginning that the Chair proposed to complete the business of the commission and present his report by the end of the year. Only a small number of meetings were planned and the dates for those meetings were agreed. Interested parties had been invited to make submissions and a trickle of submissions was coming in. A suggestion I made, that all those who made submissions should be invited to a workshop on the key issues on which the commission had been asked to report, was accepted. In the meantime, my colleagues and I at the HRB worked on our submission to the commission which was approved by the board in early-August.

The workshop for all those who made submissions was held on 26 September before the next meeting of the commission. (The issue of the second nominee of the Minister for Education was only resolved at this meeting). It was a useful exercise in that it showed that the research community was appreciative of the growth in the amount and variety of support for research. While there was support for coordination of research policy and activities, there was no support for a single research funding body. The question for the commission was how should the coordination of research policy be carried out. A visit to London and Helsinki was planned for 16-18 October so that we could see how two countries that gave a high priority to research coordinated their research policies.

In the meantime, I participated in the third week of the public health leadership programme. The theme of the week was 'facilitative leadership' in which we were coached, amongst other things, in how to facilitate agreement and in designing pathways to action. A key message was about how to develop consensus around difficult issues so that everyone could 'live' with the decision when reached. We had also been introduced to the practice of reflective writing.

The visits to London and Helsinki by the commission were helpful in clarifying thinking about the coordination of research policy. The British approach was to place great reliance on the ability of the Government's Chief Scientist 'to bang heads together' or 'to cut people off at the knees'. The Chief Scientist reported to the Prime Minister but his office was located in the Department of Industry, Trade and Employment. In Finland, a more consensual style pervaded. Coordination was through a research council, on which the Industry and Education Ministers sat. The council reported to the Prime Minister but I had the impression that most things got done by good will and a shared view of how all forms of research helped achieve the national objective.

A senior official of DETE addressed the meeting of the commission that took place in Finland on 18 October. He forcefully made the case that responsibility for coordinating national research policy should be assigned to DETE. Key arguments used were the importance of research for economic development, the legislative mandate that Department had in science and technology and the commitment of its Minister to research. During the meeting that followed a draft report prepared for the commission by external consultants was deemed unsatisfactory and the Chair requested the secretariat (provided by Forfás) to draft a new report within some guidelines proposed by the members.

The meeting of the commission on 20 November to discuss the draft report was the most rigorous of the small number held. In preparing for the meeting, I wrote reflectively the night before about the key issues, the outcome I wanted to achieve and how I felt about the meeting and the members. I also spent the night in the hotel so that my mind would be focused on the meeting. It worked well for me and I was able to make a cogent and coherent case for a system to coordinate research that respected the different reasons research is funded and its different outcomes. My favoured option was for coordination by the Department of An Taoiseach, an arrangement that has worked well in other areas such as economic and social policy where the interests of a number of departments are involved. My fall back position was to ensure that if DETE was responsible for coordination, the option favoured by a clear majority on the commission, the arrangements were sufficiently independent of the DETE and its family of organisations and sufficiently representative of the other departments with a research mandate to command the respect of all players. At the end of a long meeting I felt that considerable progress had been made. However, I was aware that until I saw the final draft, I could not relax.

The draft for discussion at the final meeting on 6 December did not provide what I considered to be a sufficient level of independence of the coordinating arrangements from the DETE. My view was shared by the representatives of the Minister for Education and Science. It was clear that the final meeting would be a difficult one. In the event, it was an extraordinary meeting. The Chair assumed that the discussion could be wrapped up in a short period. Three of the overseas members attended (a fourth participated by phone) and some of these and some of the Irish members indicated that they had planes to catch and started to leave from 09.30 onwards. On the crucial issue of the independence of the proposed coordinating arrangements, the Chair insisted on a series of votes and the proposals tabled in the draft were carried. This left me in a very awkward position. Did I sign a report in which I believed there were proposals that were not in the interest of health research or did I dissent from the recommendations of the majority, incurring personal opprobrium from members of the commission and the interests they represented? Although my preference is always to find a compromise, it did not take me long to come to a decision. My mandate was clear. I would have to indicate my lack of agreement to key aspects of the recommendations. My view was shared by a representative of the Minister for Education and Science and later that day we drafted a statement for inclusion in the final report. I spoke with the Chair of the HRB and with the Minister and received the backing from both for the content of the statement.

The statement was not well received by the majority on the commission. An effort was made to have the statement omitted from the report that went to the Minister for Enterprise, Trade and Employment but we insisted that it be included.

Despite the rush to complete the work of the commission, the report has not yet gone to Government for decision, almost one year after its completion. Discussions are still taking place between the key departmental interests about the manner in which research will be coordinated.

Could the situation have been avoided? I believe it could if the commission had paid more attention to reaching a consensus and less to completing its task on time. The price for not reaching a consensus has been a delay in bringing the recommendations to Government for decision.

And the contribution of the public health leadership course? Thanks to the course I had much greater confidence in my own judgement and ability, a greater understanding of the variety of personality types and styles that made up the commission membership, skills to analyse problems and identify pathways to action and through reflective writing, a means to focus on the most important issues and emotions arising in particular situations. No other course I have done has given me so much!

Naming the game

Anne Marie Telford

'I don't feel comfortable with the blame being placed on the person dropping the eggs', she said. We stopped, surprised. We were supposed to be working as a team – a team with a task to complete. Yet our focus was purely on winning, completing the task, being successful. We were very ready to apportion blame, to scapegoat the person who seemed to be underperforming. We would have been perfectly content to exclude this person if it would help us achieve the goal more quickly. Then we'd all look good. All except the problem person that is.

But was that the only problem? No. Did we consider how clearly we were communicating? Did we review our approach, refine our technique? No. Our reaction was to blame, scapegoat, exclude and get on with the task, anticipating the reward.

The person who spoke up, with her intervention, reminded us what being a team meant. Getting the job done and supporting each other, looking out for one another, helping each person to contribute to the success.

We were embarrassed. We knew she was right. And we had thought of ourselves as more person-focused than task-focused.

Following the intervention 'the uncoordinated one' spoke. She told us how she felt. She did not want to be excluded. She wanted to play her part, to be one of the team, to make her contribution. Had no-one noticed that others were consistently dropping eggs? Had no-one noticed the awkward 'throws'? She appreciated someone speaking out.

It's so easy to become focused on the task as we get more and more work assigned. Each task seems more important than the last, and the timescales to act ever shorter. It's easy to lose sight of others and their feelings – to forget about the impact of our words and actions on colleagues, on friends, on family. It's easy for the task to take over and when things aren't quite right to find someone to blame.

The person who had spoken out made us all see what was happening in the group – she had 'named the behaviour'. How powerful. It's so much more comfortable to observe and say nothing – go with the crowd. At best make a joke of it but certainly never acknowledge it head on. But by taking action, by drawing attention to the unhelpful behaviour this made us stand back and reconsider. We weren't told to change – we each decided to change.

Speaking out required courage. It made a difference. It was a real act of leadership. We all learned a lot.

The Ring – a metaphor for the public health network

Eleanor Gill

The ring is amazingly and simply perfect in its shape – round, strong, connected and unbreakable. In Irish the word for round and exact is the same: 'cruinn'. It is derived from the time when our ancestors made wheels for chariots and carriages. When the wheel was exact in its shape or 'dead on' it was referred to as 'cruinn'.

Although the ring is a common shape it accommodates diversity. It comes in different metals and decorations: colourful stones and treasured jewels are set within the circle.

The ring represents a contract, a partnership – a loving bond which lasts through time, growing, adversity, change. It necessitates commitment, dedication and investment.

The ring is deeply symbolic and steeped in mythology and history. It is fondly passed down from generation to generation – a precious legacy.

The public health network embraces the power of the ring.

A Promise

Helen Whelton

Promise to Sean

Sitting on a flight from Cork to Belfast having left the office under an hour ago, I have time to sit back, relax and ... I promised Sean 1,000 words on my leadership challenge! OH MY GOD!!! Forget relaxation, or maybe not, maybe relax, think of Gillie Bolton and her reflective practice and let the words flow.

The context

I feel privileged to have been part of the Institute of Public Health's magnificent leadership programme. I learned so much, not just from the wonderful interactive courses but from the network developed. I met many new inspiring people and found further inspiration within those I knew already. As well as team building skills, I learned to recognise the support all around me. The encouragement to adopt a cause and take on a particular leadership challenge was daunting for many reasons. Firstly, the thought of taking on extra work of a large scale was off-putting. The idea of expressing current work-in-hand as a leadership challenge seemed to violate the relationships amongst the team – regular work doesn't present itself as neat leadership challenges which you can present in a neatly packaged 1,000 word summary. It doesn't have a beginning, middle and end; it is constant and never ending.

Leadership challenge...school milk revival

In any case I decided to go outside of my academic environment and apply my skills in the outside world. My challenge emerged as a result of my membership of the Parents' Association of my son's school. At one of our regular meetings one mother raised the issue of school milk. The school had abandoned the programme to distribute subsidised school milk the previous year. The committee unanimously agreed that the school should be encouraged to reinstate the programme. I was asked to research the background and elucidate the reasons for the abandonment of the scheme and the potential for reinstatement. My main interest in the challenge was from a health promotion perspective.

The main issues were:

- Children benefit from calcium and protein in milk.
- Milk displaces fruit drinks from the lunchbox.
- Fruit drinks and soft drinks are perceived to be healthy but
    - (a) contain sugar and cause dental caries, and
    - (b) have a low pH and can cause irreversible dental erosion.
- From an oral health perspective water and milk are the only drinks which are safe for teeth.

Situation analysis

Many phone calls later the following facts were apparent:

- EU subsidises school milk.
- Dairies facilitate its delivery.
- The National Dairy Council (NDC) provides refrigeration for milk bought from NDC subscriber dairies.
- The school milk programme is in decline. NDC reports decline in uptake.
- The local dairy have a schools liaison person to facilitate schools in the distribution of milk.

I discussed the challenge of addressing the decline in uptakes of school milk with the principals of my son's and my daughter's schools. I already had a good rapport with these principals as I have engaged with them many times.

The chalenges were identified as follows:

- Danger of breakage of glass bottles.
- Residual milk when container changed from ⅓ pint bottle to ⅓ litre carton.
- Cartons not environmentally friendly.
- Disposal of cartons – charges.

Communication with the schools liaison person revealed that her perception was that the real barrier in the schools was the administrative burden on teachers who had to dispense the milk. She described a number of dispensing options to avoid the use of cartons.

Error of judgement...

At the next meeting of the Parents' Association I presented my situation analysis with options for addressing the barriers reported by the principal. It was agreed that I should bring these options to the Board of Management, of which I was also a member.

That was an error of judgement. I brought the topic up under any other business. I presented the case, reasons why we should have school milk, barriers to the implementation of the programme as described by the principal and solutions to the problems identified. My suggestions went down like a lead balloon. The principal was completely taken by surprise and was not willing to either accept or reject the proposal. I suggested that he consult with the teachers, feeling at the same time that there was zero support. Lesson: I should have consulted with him before the meeting.

There is more than one way to skin a cat

I reported my setback to my fellow parents at the next meeting and suggested that we await further feedback from the principal. I intended taking up the issue again once the dust had settled. However, I was not hopeful of a positive response.

The chairman and secretary of our group had a meeting with the teachers shortly after, with the aim of identifying areas where the association could support the activities of the teachers. The chairman broached the subject of the school milk with the teachers and put forward the suggestions which I had brought to the group. The teachers were very enthusiastic about the scheme and agreed to implement one of the options. The local dairy now delivers to the school bags of milk which are attached to refrigerated dispensers. Special cups are provided which the children bring home every evening to be washed. The principal seems proud to be associated with the programme and is now an enthusiastic supporter.

How did the leadership programme impact on this experience

This pilot 'school milk revival' leadership challenge has shown me the value of engaging the consumer and of rallying support amongst people in key positions outside the health services in an indirect manner. You cannot hustle schools into doing what you as a health care person want them to do. Because of the leadership programme I reflected on every step of this process. Instead of ploughing on with what I was doing, I took time to think about people's reactions to what was happening. I view this small project as a mirror of what is happening in public services. We have many disciplines working independently towards their own or their organisational goals. These goals are ultimately the same, that is to improve people's quality of life through, for example, education, parenting, health care or nutrition. We can achieve our goals with greater ease and efficiency if we work as a network. The leadership programme introduced me to a North/South network that I could not have previously enjoyed. Within this network I gained an appreciation of the great commonality amongst the members. Looking outside the leadership programme network I now have a greater insight into the extent of support surrounding me when I am working to achieve progress towards a goal that is shared by many other disciplines. The theory of the benefits of a common risk factor approach in health promotion has been well known to me for some time. This programme gave substance to the theory, the reality exceeded expectations.

I researched the school milk issue in our local school, I presented a range of options to my fellow parents. They trusted me as part of their group and valued the work I had done towards resolving an issue which they had raised as a problem. In turn, when the opportunity arose, they presented the options for change to the teachers, who in a non-threatening parent/teacher setting were very pleased to help. This was a soft approach.

The theory of this approach to empowering communities is very familiar. The reality creates a powerful impression. The boys of St Joseph's now receive chilled milk on a daily basis – with the exception of my son who has a milk allergy!

Next challenges

- How to address the national situation.
- How to engage parents' associations and encourage them to work with the teachers to reintroduce the scheme (via National Parents Council?).

Other interesting observations

- No one owns this issue.
- There was no 'one stop shop' for help.
- The Minister for Health and Children is interested in promoting the school milk scheme.
- Bord Glas is interested in the scheme.
- Dental services – Northern Ireland is interested.
- Only 20% of schoolchildren avail of the scheme.

Clouds

Karen Meehan

My project was to secure the involvement of voluntary and community groups in the process of developing *Other Borders*, a cross border health strategy for women from the northwest, aiming to impact on emotional health and mental wellbeing. It was launched in June 2003.

The development of *Other Borders* began in October 2000 following a process designed to ensure we got buy-in from stakeholder agencies from the outset and that the final document would be evidence-based and research-led.

The plan seemed fairly sound apart from the omission of voluntary/community sector agencies from the stakeholder group.

I always knew that I would try and secure the involvement of community and voluntary groups in *Other Borders* at some stage. But before beginning the process of involving them I decided to secure the buy-in of statutory agencies. This decision caused me to have to deal with my own demons and doubts, triggered by resistance I encountered in some sections of the voluntary sector, which was occasionally personal and painful. I remember leaving one particular meeting with my confidence a bit further undermined that this 'hard' project couldn't be done. Stronger than the dented confidence though was the determination to do it some way, somehow. However the experience of negativity about the planned process confirmed my hunch to begin by securing the involvement of the statutory agencies.

During the process of talking to statutory agencies I was trying and failing to convince one of the stakeholders of my rationale, ie, that the initial buy-in of statutory agencies was vital to ensure that *Other Borders* would actually be implemented. Their buy-in was also necessary to convince the often overstretched community sector of the worth of investing their scarce capacity.

During this period two things happened around the same time. I moved into the second phase (consultation) of the development of *Other Borders* and I learned about 'clouds' (from the theory of constraints, an approach to problem solving).

At Inchydoney, during a residential part of the leadership programme, I worked with my small group practising using 'clouds' to deal with the resistance I was encountering. When I returned to Derry a phone conversation with the stakeholder ended up resolving the difficulties we had been experiencing.

I still don't know whether it was the cloud thing or the fact I was now at the stage of involving voluntary and community groups through the consultation exercise, either way something shifted and I developed a close and mutually supportive relationship with previously disgruntled statutories. They worked hard to ensure their organisation was really engaged with the project.

Our 'clash' had really rocked and at times probably angered me. This whole project to develop *Other Borders* had terrified me. (There were times, especially at the beginning when I hoped I would get ill enough to allow me to walk away).

It was so big (both in terms of geography and remit) and hard. I knew that because I had developed it, I felt the need to demonstrate to people that my being lucky enough to get seconded from my role as Co-Coordinator of Derry Well Woman did not mean that I was getting a holiday. I made it hard for myself both from guilt (that Derry Well Woman had agreed an internal restructure to accommodate my move into the project) and gratitude (to Derry Well Woman and to funders who were supporting me). The problems with the stakeholder had chipped away at my already dodgy confidence in my ability to do this 'hard' project.

Looking back, there were two things I learned about myself on the first residential week of the public health leadership course that I wanted to address: having a desire to be liked and having difficulty managing conflict. The difficulties I experienced tapped into both and maybe shoved me somewhat along the road to maturity! In fact the experience was one of growth and learning and it makes me happy to think about it.

When we moved into the consultation phase of the process, a research team was commissioned to carry out the consultation. We decided that the extent of engagement with the process would be enhanced if we could link with local groups throughout the eight council areas covered by *Other Borders*. I developed a list of eighty-four voluntary and community groups from Limavady to Leitrim with whom I was to make contact to request help.

When I did begin to contact them, my efforts to involve the community and voluntary sectors were met with open arms. I believe every one of the eighty-four groups I contacted participated. I think I contacted them all individually, went down and visited many of them and obviously covered all costs (childcare, travel, hospitality) associated with their involvement.

I spent time describing the project to them, asked them to think about getting involved and then facilitated their chosen method of input ie, as focus group, convenor or distributor of general populative questionnaires. Early on in the process a number of groups stated that they were sick of being consulted in academic exercises that had no impact on their daily lives, which were carried out by people who never returned once they had drained the community of their views.

I promised two things; that we (the research team) would feed back to communities before signing off the final report to ensure that they were happy with our analysis, and also that *Other Borders* would literally and directly address their priorities. We delivered on both of these promises.

Finally, when we asked groups why they got involved (especially at a time of consultation fatigue) they responded that in addition to a commitment to the women's health agenda, the compelling things for them were the facts that (i) leadership was being taken by a voluntary sector organisation and (ii) that stakeholders were already around the table and committed to acting on what they said. They had confidence that *Other Borders* would make a difference.

Candid camera

Eleanor Gill

Who's going to be in the photograph? I tremble inside. I know that a mistake here could take away from all that the team has achieved. So many people to please, so many balls to juggle, what do I do?

Being a leader can be really lonely! Partnership working can really hurt!

And then on to the competition ...

What a sound, what an arrangement! The team are playing like a first-class orchestra. I look down the row at their proud and beaming faces – they really believe in this, they want to tell their story, share their learning. Their eyes are dancing and alive! What a class act – we have won! Spontaneously we all hug and kiss each other – this is real. This feeling should be bottled and shared.

Being a leader is really rewarding! Partnership working is worth the effort!

No beginning too small

Jane Wilde

So, what's it like setting up an organisation?

Exciting, challenging, satisfying and exhausting.

But what's the story?

I was taken downstairs to the basement. It was early September 1998. Earlier I had stepped out of the station to the warmth of a late summer's day. I noticed roses fading in the flower beds, several weeks ahead of those in my own garden.

Dublin seemed a foreign city. What was I doing here? Working for the first time in the capital city of Ireland.

Walking beside the Liffey, along the cobbled path in front of the Custom House, I was trying to adjust to a new geography. Looking up to search for landmarks, the pale green plate glass of Hawkins House. I'd been there several years before with the Chief Medical Officer from Northern Ireland to meet his equivalent, to discuss the possibility of an all-island Institute of Public Health.

There was no 'real' meeting, no 'real' discussion. More like a pleasant chat, with large plates of salad and salmon balanced precariously on our knees while we chatted rather aimlessly – or so it seemed.

We missed the train and sat for hours in a dark, dusty Connolly Station.

But progress was made and the idea, once planted, survived political, bureaucratic and financial hurdles.

I was shown into a small broom cupboard in the basement:

Windows – none.

Furniture – two lovely round-backed old leather dining room chairs.

Lighting – a caterpillar of plastic snaking its way round the ceiling.

Equipment – dust on an old computer, missing parts, on a rickety table in the corner.

'We had planned that the Institute would move to the new extension. But other staff are there now. We thought you'd fit here!'

(No denying that, there was only me)

The first year was taken up with meetings with many individuals and organisations in all parts of the island: discussion, debate, disagreement, argument, drafting and redrafting. Every word of the document had to be checked and the process began to resemble the negotiations before the Good Friday Agreement.

At last a clear document outlining our vision, our objectives and our workplan.

Preparing our first strategy was a chance to put into practice our beliefs about public health. To describe our vision and what we, a newly formed all-Ireland Institute could do to achieve it.

Our logo reminded me of the bridges I crossed each day – over the Lagan and the Liffey. Symbolic of the bridges that the Institute needed to cross – geographic, professional and sectoral. Others saw in it a reflective eye, a mirror, a circle, offering, I hoped, a picture of an Institute which would provide space for people to share and develop their understanding of public health.

It was from the basement that we planned the Institute's launch: 19 November 1999.

A beautiful display of chrysanthemums, autumn leaves and berries in shades of crimson and burnt orange sat on a pedestal at the foot of the college staircase, chosen to match the colours on the cover of our first strategy document and to reflect our newly designed logo.

A huge number gathered at our launch in the Corrigan Hall. The warmth of support was overwhelming.

Four years on from the launch, I am proud of our achievements. We have held our initial vision and worked hard in our efforts to reach it. We have made tackling health inequalities the focus of all our work, and put into practice our belief in multidisciplinary and multi-sectoral work. We now have staff with a variety of backgrounds, experiences and nationalities working together in our new offices in Belfast and Dublin.

We have developed strong relationships with people in public health throughout Ireland.

We are crossing borders and boundaries, continuing to practise our beliefs and commitment to public health.

We have tried to change some paradigms, to reflect this in our work, to encourage others to join with us and to produce good and thoughtful work which is making a difference to the health of people across the island.

Bridges

Gillie Bolton

Her hand on my arm
so I can be eyes for us both
on the stony path by the river,
she stops, *look at the arch*
of the old bridge, and its reflection.
I can't see it, but can you?

The reflection wavers as a duck passes;
stone arch, and reflected arch together
make a perfect circle.

We've written together, shared pools
of deep thought, mirroring our lives
yet different: the one reflecting the other
touching, feeling, tasting, listening,
seeing beyond sight.

'We must learn to live together
as brothers or perish together
as fools.'

Martin Luther King Jr

Challenging orthodoxies

The final set of pieces all have something of
the polemic about them. They seek to
challenge sacred cows, the status quo and
conventional wisdom. The ability to do this
must be a key part of successful leadership.
Achieving a healthy society cannot be done
without questioning often powerful forces,
who do not have the health and wellbeing of
people as their bottom line. Readers may find
themselves both inspired and enraged, but
hopefully stimulated and ready to enter into
the debates.

A healthy society through healthy organisations: physician heal thyself

Sean Denyer

A man sits crumpled in a chair. I hand him another tissue.
He looks both defeated and embarrassed at the same time. He sits
on the edge of the chair, slightly bent over, eyes to the floor.
We sit in silence for another couple of minutes before he speaks,

'If I hadn't been doing a good job, why didn't someone tell me?
Just why didn't they tell me?'

A woman, middle aged and dressed in a navy blue suit, hits her
fist hard against the desk. She looks angry. Her face flushed and
her mouth drawn tight as a bowstring ready to fire a lethal arrow.

'I have been working all the hours God sends, neglecting my kids
and coming in on weekends, missing family stuff I should have
been at and for what? To be told, after three years, that there were
serious concerns about the project. But I kept telling them there
were problems and no one wanted to listen. Now the shit has hit
the fan and they want a scapegoat!'

A man shuffles the papers on his desk, leans back in his chair and
sighs. He looks worried, pre-occupied, drumming his fingers on
the armrest of his chair.

'I know that something is going seriously wrong in the surgical
department. I mentioned it to the senior management and they
just looked like deer caught in the headlights. They want to avoid
a media controversy like they had in the other place. They are just
hoping that if they bury their heads in the sand it will go away.
But it won't.'

A woman sips her coffee, looking tired and drawn, her feet
tapping the tiled floor.

'A thank you would have been nice. I know it's my job, but I put in a lot of extra effort and time that they weren't even aware of. I wouldn't do it again.'

A man in a suit, belly hanging over his belt, top button undone, tie loosened, props up the bar. He downs his fifth pint of the evening. Lights a cigar.

'Sure after the week I've had I'll be needing a few more of these! Driven a thousand miles this week, been in the High Court, and the boss wants the paper on 'Achieving a Healthier Life/Work Balance' by Monday for the board meeting. I'll be working all weekend!'

Though these people are all fictional their experiences are real. Composites drawn from different people in different situations. It would be surprising if anyone reading this didn't relate to them and flinch slightly at the memory.

Though the stories are different they have some common features. A failure of communication, a lack of clarity, reluctance to deal with inter-personal conflict, an absence of feedback, good or bad.

It is often said that the reason that we don't have a healthier society is because of a lack of vision. Whilst accepting the partial truth of this, I would argue that we are much more handicapped by our lack of leadership. The experiences of the people described here are symptoms of that.

Undertaking the leadership programme gave me an opportunity to reflect on the many different aspects of leadership, and suggested to me that to develop a healthier society we need to get much better at communicating the vision and breaking it down into manageable components that are understood by the people given the task of implementing it. The changes we think may be needed come through requiring people to change either through legislation or by encouragement, education or persuasion. Even legislation needs people to frame it and then enforce it. Building a healthier society means helping people help other people change.

If people do not understand what they are doing and why they are doing it then mistakes are more likely. If people make mistakes and are punished they are more likely to be hidden. If people hide things then a whole culture of collusion can develop which, though as fragile a house of cards, may seem preferable to the mess that is left when it falls.

A healthier society can only come through the people in it working together to develop it. Yet all too often we are not role modelling with our own staff the very qualities that will bring about the changes we want.

Is a healthy society one where people have little time for their families or for getting involved in their communities? Is it one that punishes people for making a mistake instead of learning from it? Is it one that expects people to work in the dark with no idea of where they are going? Is it one that is rigid and inflexible and doesn't take account of different demands at different stages of people's lives? Is it one that writes off age and experience and yet fears youthful energy? Is it one that doesn't celebrate achievements? Is it one that fails to protect people or develop systems that prevent errors happening in the first place?

I don't think such a society could be called healthy.

The man who cried was doing a bad job. A job for which he hadn't been trained and was temperamentally unsuited for. He is still doing it.

The woman with the fist left the health service and has developed a successful business.

The pre-occupied man blew the whistle on what was going on, and has had to move to a new job, uprooting his family.

The woman who sipped the coffee is still in the same job. She remains unthanked.

The man with the cigar is stressed no longer. Massive heart attack. He is dead.

Public health before private profit

Joe Barry

January 2002 saw the birth of the Strategic Task Force on Alcohol and of the public health leadership programme. The first two years of each have been marked by much development and many surprises, and the period from January 2004 onwards can be even more productive, if the learning continues. I am the only common link between the two processes, and their simultaneous development has meant that my input into the Task Force has been enriched and hopefully enhanced.

A meaningful improvement in Ireland vis-a-vis alcohol can only come about through a truly massive cultural shift. If we learn from history, always assumed to be easier than it is, then the prospects for the next decade being better than the 1990s are good. If the pointers for change are ignored, consciously or unconsciously, then the future is easy to predict, and not very pleasant. Because prophets of doom generally are a turn-off, it is necessary when acting as an advocate in relation to alcohol to be humorous, resourceful and imaginative – and to take risks. One key issue in alcohol advocacy is the relationship between the drinks industry and policy makers; and how to keep clear water between the two. Beware of those offering partnership, when partnership is not what is required. Alcohol advocacy is also about reclaiming the primacy of politics from free marketeers who seek to buy, successfully so far in this country, commercial advantage.

Let us not have a 30 year debate on whether we need to do something to improve our health with regard to alcohol, as we have had with tobacco. Let us persuade our politicians that public health is more important than private profit.

When clearing out my parents' home recently I came across an article from the Irish Independent of April 1968. My parents bought their house in 1968 and the newspaper had lain hidden for 35 years, functioning as a drawer liner. The article concerned the introduction of the breathalyser in the UK. The new law was opposed at the time by brewers who claimed that breath testing of drivers had affected their trade drastically. Mrs Barbara Castle – a conviction politician – was unmoved by their lobbying and was instead impressed by the substantial drop in road accidents. So were the British public: Mrs Castle came out on top shortly afterwards in a public opinion poll on the popularity of government ministers.

Back to the 21st Century and the Strategic Task Force! The behaviour of the British brewers in 1968 was replicated by the Irish Drinks Industry Group – regrettably now with two representatives on the Strategic Task Force – in 2002, when they issued a minority statement in relation to some of the recommendations of the Task Force; in particular, one that would have reduced our drink driving blood alcohol limit from 80mg% to 50mg%. Shadow structures and covert lobbying are alive and well in Irish alcohol policy-making.

Confronting, in a personalised way, drinks industry representatives who are individually pleasant, is not something that comes easily but, unfortunately, it has got to be done. I hope the leadership programme will keep me energised to continue. Twelve years of work in the illicit drugs field has not given me experience or practice at confronting suppliers who come smiling. Heroin dealers or tobacco barons are much easier to oppose.

I am now the proud possessor of a letter from the CEO/President of Anheuser-Busch International Inc. The letter came to me in July with a complimentary copy of a book entitled *The Social Norms Approach to Preventing School and College Age Substance Abuse*. Luckily, I also have a briefing paper prepared by the American Medical Association(AMA) entitled 'Partner or Foe? The Alcohol Industry, Youth Alcohol Problems and Alcohol Policy Strategies'. The AMA has carried out a devastating critique of the social norms approach adopted by the drinks industry in America.

From the 1997 Anheuser-Busch annual report: 'Every action taken…by management is guided by an overriding objective…enhancing shareholder value'. These actions gave Anheuser-Busch a net income in 2000 in excess of 1.5 billion dollars. You can see why the words of the CEO/President in his letter to me of July 2003, 'we look forward to making an ongoing, effective contribution in Ireland' fill me with horror. The drinks industry does 'effective' very well; however, it is very much at variance with my type of 'effective'.

Our indigenous drinks industry is at the same business. MEAS (conceived as 'Managing the Enjoyment of Alcohol in Society' but now trading as 'Mature Enjoyment of Alcohol in Society') has been set up by the drinks industry to do what drinks industry groups do everywhere – Minimise Effective Action by the State. Public health leaders are required urgently to counteract and expose their efforts. The billions of Euro spent by the industry on promotions, marketing and advertising need to be counterbalanced by flair and imagination in backing up the much more meagre resources devoted to health promotion.

To change culture is a big thing; it requires energy, drive, support and long-term thinking, together with a belief that things must change. The depth of the change that is required was brought home to me recently – again by an item I came across while sorting through my late father's effects. The item was a letter to him from a government minister of about ten years ago, in response apparently to a letter he had written complaining about a rumour of the Government's plan to lower the blood alcohol limit for driving from 80mg% to 50mg%. The letter from the minister reassured my father that the Government had no wish to diminish the pub culture in Ireland and did not foresee lowering the blood alcohol limit. Ten years on, the blood alcohol limit is still 80mg%, the drinks industry is still lobbying to keep it at that, but hopefully the response that a letter similar to my father's would elicit today would be different.

Cultural change can be a good thing; indeed it is necessary if current culture is having negative consequences. It is possible to retain the positive aspects of our relationship with alcohol – bonhomie, sociability and relaxation – while limiting the harm caused to us as a people. This, however, should be done on our terms, not on the terms of the multi-national drinks industry.

Why wasn't I there?

Carolyn Mason

There is a horrible image of a man injured in a bomb – I think
it was the Oxford Street Bus Station bomb in the early 1970s.
It's a black and white photo and there is blood streaming down
his face. The whites of his eyes stand out. In 1970, I was 16
years old.

Leaders are those who turn up.

So why wasn't I there?

So many days each week I'm there
In the ordinariness of waiting for a bus in
Bleak, wet, depressing queues, by a
Sad, dark counter with newspapers, sweets, Marlboros,
chewing gum.

But that day, I'm not there.

His eyes, in the headlines, billboards, from behind the
glass screens of TVs
With thick, sticky blood in
Black and white
Gouge through mine, which
Look away, because
I'm not there.

Why didn't I speak?

Carolyn Mason

I want a political voice, but
Politics is sectarian, sectarian is politics.
Politics is sick.
I am sickened by politicians
Angered by their shrill self righteousness
Fundamental hatred
Fear of each
Other.

I switch it off, turn it over, blank it out –
I am not there
I do not speak

Therefore I am guilty.

Most of my friends left Northern Ireland at that time
to go to universities in England and Scotland.
None of them have returned.

Public health leadership
and the Nanny State

Ivan Perry

> '*A vision without a task is but a dream,*
> *a task without a vision is drudgery,*
> *a vision and a task is the hope of the world.*'
>
> Anon 1730

The folly of public health

You could say that I stumbled into public health via clinical
medicine and epidemiology. As a medical student I had a vague
and largely negative concept of the discipline that I now regard
as the architecture for a healthy society and a health-sustaining
planet. In my journey from youthful scepticism to middle-aged
idealism, I met and was changed by public health leaders such
as Geoffrey Rose and Gerry Shaper, physicians who had moved
from the care of patients at the bedside and clinic to work on
the health of nations. The public health leadership programme has
challenged me to consider what contribution I can make to the
health of our nation and beyond, specifically to define and clarify
my vision of public health and decide where and how best to
apply my enthusiasm and hope. I have also been challenged in
recent months to address the notion of the 'nanny state', in the
context of an ongoing debate on the appropriate role of the state
versus the individual in tackling public health problems such as
smoking and obesity. Molière could have been talking about
public health when he referred to 'une folie à nulle autre seconde,
de vouloir se mêler à corriger le monde', a stupidity second to

none, to want to busy oneself with the correction of the world. Clearly in public health we are not unique in this folly, or in the scale of our ambition or vision. However, we need to reflect carefully on how well we deliver on our vision, on our simple but big idea that prevention is better than cure. William Foege, writing in the *Oxford Textbook of Public Health* (2002), reminds us that in the history of mankind few ideas have attracted such support in the abstract and neglect in practice as the primacy of prevention.

The problem with eggs

To paraphrase Foege, our society seems almost immune to the simple notion that it is easy to scramble but impossible to unscramble an egg. We invest heavily in expensive end-stage care in intensive care units, while failing to invest in relatively inexpensive measures that would add quality years to life. This is a source of frustration to all of us who work in public health. The problem in part lies with man's innate tendency to discount the future, to value x amount of happiness in the present over the possibility of x plus y happiness in the future. However, the low priority accorded to prevention in our society must be regarded, at least in part, as a failure of public health leadership, a failure to sell the idea of prevention. For a big idea to change society it requires a movement or organisation that is focused, confident and well-organised, adjectives that do not immediately spring to mind when we consider the public health movement in Ireland or internationally. Ideas that change the world generally challenge established institutions and structures. We seem reluctant to even quantify the imbalance in resource allocation between prevention and treatment within our health system. With the notable exception of the tobacco industry, we have failed to prioritise and focus our efforts on the major threats to health within our local communities and the ever-shrinking global community, threats such as the marketing of junk food to children, the proliferation of private car ownership or large class sizes in primary schools. It seem to me that at the heart of contemporary public health practice, lies the need to identify threats to health locally and globally, to rank them in order of importance and to mobilise the necessary resources to tackle the most important problems, confronting if necessary vested interests inimical to health.

I believe we take on too much in public health. We need to be more selective in the problems we tackle. While it is important to understand the determinants of health, and to highlight the injustice of health inequalities, we need to focus on enlisting or mobilising support for tangible societal level measures that will produce measurable improvements in the health of the population.

Echoes from the past

To develop these arguments further, I have found it helpful to consider how this notion of public health fits with current concepts and definitions of the discipline. I have also considered the extent to which our concept of public health has changed over the centuries. There is no universally agreed, accessible definition of public health. In recent decades, erudite committees in several countries (including Ireland) have deliberated on the nature and purpose of public health. In 1988 the US Institute of Medicine established a 'committee for the study of the future of public health'. The committee concluded that public health was not clearly defined, fully understood or adequately supported. It was noted that the demand for public health is framed in different ways, including public health as a profession, a governmental activity and a commitment to the betterment of society. Little has changed in the intervening years. In the US, as in Ireland and elsewhere, most people associate public health with the provision of health services for the poor.

Our current perception and understanding of public health needs to be set within a broader historical context. Hamlin (2002) has argued that public health is a central element of the history of the developed world, as it is in health terms that our lives are most profoundly different from those of our ancestors. In developed countries most of us do not live our lives racked with chronic pain, with abscesses or deformities. We do not see life as a continuously painful experience with death as a merciful release, a view that was fairly widespread up to the 17th century. Surprisingly, despite the central role of health in our lives and in the progress of nations, public health is a largely invisible part of our past and discussion of health issues in contemporary societies is partial and largely focused on health services. At the risk of gross over-simplification, the history of public health can be conceived in terms of three relatively distinct missions: public health as reaction to epidemics such as plague; public health as a form of police or community regulation designed to protect the institutions of the state including the military who needed an adequate supply of healthy recruits; and, since the 18th century, public health as a means of betterment, a proactive political vision for the improvement of the health of the population, (Hamlin 2002). Unfortunately, the earlier impoverished concepts of public health have not receded completely and the vision of a healthy society is invariably distorted to some extent by political ideology, in particular the prevailing view on the size and role of the state. Thus, echoes of history reverberate in contemporary public health developments. In the US, for instance, we see a resurgence of interest in developing a public health infrastructure in response to the threat of bio-terrorism. The World Bank monitors population health indices in the developing world because health is now regarded as an essential prerequisite for economic development. By contrast, the WHO Framework Convention on tobacco control reflects a proactive political movement focused on reducing the burden of suffering and death due to tobacco. However, enthusiasm and support for the Convention varies markedly internationally and it is unlikely to be ratified by the US and other administrations on the conservative, 'libertarian' end of the political spectrum.

Detels and Breslow (1997) drawing on this notion of public health as a political vision for the betterment of society, have defined public health in simple terms as the process of mobilising local, state (regional), national and international resources to ensure the conditions in which people can be healthy. This is a simple but powerful concept of public health. It incorporates the notion of empowerment and the need for those of us working in public health to forge alliances across all sectors of society in pursuit of our objectives. It is focused on positive health, action-oriented and inclusive of the full spectrum of public health and health promotion and health advocacy activities. The goals for public health that follow from this definition of the discipline are to identify and prioritise problems that affect entire communities or populations, to marshal support to address these problems and to ensure that the solutions are implemented. To achieve these goals we need adequately resourced population health information systems and a multi-disciplinary public health workforce with the skills to interpret and use health information to empower individuals and communities and change the policies of governments. Linked to these resources we need to develop explicit population health performance standards that will translate our aspirations into actions. These are the basics. However, for public health to flourish, there is an additional critical ingredient, a political consensus on the role of the state in protecting the health of individuals and communities. Unfortunately, when public health measures threaten vested interests, especially commercial interests, the spectre of the 'nanny state' is raised, the notion that the state should not interfere with our personal choice in matters related to health, such as our diet or alcohol consumption. This raises a key issue for public health, the balance between the rights of the state and the individual.

The 'nanny state'

The most conservative, free market liberals must accept that governments play a major role in protecting and promoting the health of the people. For instance, in Dublin infant mortality fell from 157 per 1,000 of the estimated population under one year to 6 per 1,000 between 1913 and the turn of the century. Even in recent decades we have seen substantial gains in population health. Between 1975 and 1997 male life expectancy in Ireland increased by almost 6 years to 74.6 years and female life expectancy by 5 years to 78.6 years. The improvements we have seen in the health of the population in Ireland and other developed countries over the past century have been achieved primarily through broad societal level measures including improvements in sanitation, nutrition, housing, employment conditions and education, and reductions in absolute and relative poverty. Despite these improvements, we continue to experience high mortality rates from preventable conditions including heart disease, cancer, accidents and suicide. We have the highest mortality from heart disease in the European Union and the lowest life expectancy at age 65. In this century, as in the last, poverty and social status remain critical determinants of health, with over two-fold higher mortality rates among people in poorly-paid occupations relative to those in professional and other highly-paid occupations.

The health service provides a vital safety net when we are ill but in practice makes a relatively small contribution to protecting and promoting positive health and wellbeing and preventing premature death. Most people intuitively understand and accept the role of the state in safeguarding our health by, for instance, insisting on acceptable standards of food hygiene in the hospitality industry, prohibiting driving whilst under the influence of alcohol or drugs, or requiring compliance with speed limits on our roads. Few would argue that involvement of the state in these areas represents an unacceptable infringement on our personal freedom or interference with our civil liberties. Unfortunately, however, when the state intervenes to protect the health of the population in a way that threatens commercial vested interests, the spectre of the nanny state is raised. The debate in 2003 on the proposal to ban smoking in all work-places, including bars and restaurants, provides a clear example of this phenomenon. Smoking causes approximately 5 million deaths worldwide each year, including approximately 7,000 deaths in Ireland. As a cause of death in this country it dwarfs all other factors in our external environment. Paradoxically, because deaths from smoking are so common, our reaction is muted. As George Eliot put it in Middlemarch, 'we do not expect people to be deeply moved by what is not unusual. That element of tragedy which lies in the very fact of frequency,

has not yet wrought itself into the coarse emotion of mankind.'
Faced with a Minister for Health & Children who is genuinely
committed to tackling this scourge, opponents in the 'Hospitality
Alliance' claimed that he should focus on the 'real problems' of
the health service such as waiting lists and over-crowded accident
and emergency departments. Unfortunately, this response is
unsurprising given the obsessional focus on health services in
discussion of health issues in this country.

The fat tax

The chorus of criticism, bordering on ridicule, that greeted the
recent (2003) suggestion from Deputy Batt O'Keeffe, Chairman
of the Oireachtas Sub-Committee on Health and Children, that
Ireland should consider a fat tax, provides a further illustration of
this phenomenon. It is estimated that by 2030 almost 50% of the
US population will meet current criteria for clinical obesity.
Ireland is not far behind the US in this matter with
approximately one quarter of middle-aged men and women
exceeding the clinical obesity threshold and clear evidence of an
emerging epidemic of obesity in childhood and adolescence.
As a society we must now choose between taking measures to
tackle this epidemic or simply watch it unfold. If (as seems likely)
we take the latter option, we had better plan for major increases
in resources for patients with obesity-related diabetes and kidney
failure and we will need to match our US cousins in facilities for
the surgical treatment of 'morbid obesity'. Although our health
and life expectancy have improved steadily over the past century,
it is not an immutable law of nature that these favourable trends
will continue in an environment designed to maximise calorie
intake and restrict opportunities for exercise.

It is now clear from several decades of research that preventive
strategies focussed on simply alerting the population to the health
problems of obesity will not turn the tide of this epidemic. In the
context of the obesity epidemic in childhood, it is estimated that
in 1999 the food industry in the UK spent Stg£300 million
creating advertisements designed to capture children's

imaginations and specifically to encourage them to buy or ask for foods that are high in sugar, salt and fat. While we may debate the merits of fat, sugar or salt taxes, it is clear that we need to consider some measures as a society to restrict our exposure to food that is damaging our health and that of our children. For instance, there is no reason why we should not emulate Sweden where advertising targeted at children under ten is prohibited. We might also consider tightening food labeling regulations so that people know how much saturated fat, salt and sugar is in their diet. The option of fiscal measures that would discourage the food industry from producing and aggressively marketing unhealthy products should also remain open. To adopt such measures is hardly a manifestation of the 'nanny state', 'health fascism' or naïve utopianism, but merely enlightened self-preservation. Clearly, there are no easy solutions to the looming epidemics of chronic disease linked to obesity and lack of exercise. To re-engineer our environment, including our cities, buildings, workplaces and homes in a way that will help us walk more and eat less will require a clear long-term strategy, broad societal or multi-sectoral involvement, and long-term sustained investment. At the very least we should accept that although we have personal responsibility for our own health and that of our children, there is a limit to what can be achieved without societal change. In essence, it will be hard for our children to avoid putting on weight and to acquire healthy eating habits if we continue to design our towns and cities around the car and if every time they go to the cinema they are presented with a tub of popcorn and a small bucket of cola. Unfortunately, the motor, food and entertainment industries are unlikely to embrace a public health agenda. We will need to mobilise the required resources to confront these vested interests, to reframe transport, food policy and related issues in health terms.

Means and ends

As a society we fret obsessionally over the health of the economy. We monitor growth rates, inflation, unemployment rates and a host of other indices. Amartya Sen, the Nobel prize winning economist, reminds us that economics is about means not ends. This may be our challenge as public health leaders, the core task for our discipline, to hold our government accountable for the health of the people as well as the health of our economy. Rudolph Virchow, the 18th century pathologist, is well known to medical students for his work on the mechanisms of blood clots. He is less well known for his dictum: 'Medicine is a social science, and politics nothing but medicine on a grand scale'.

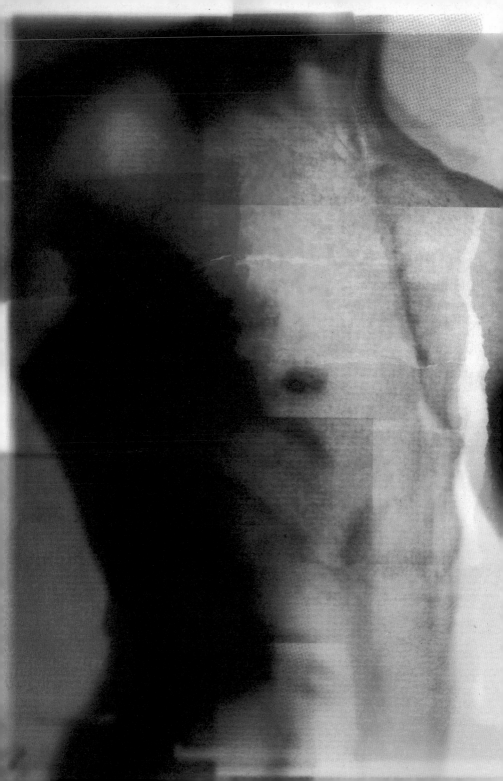

Men's health – lost years – preventable or inevitable?

Owen Metcalfe

What all the world is made of

What are little girls made of?
Sugar and spice and all things nice,
That's what little girls are made of;
What are little boys made of?
Slugs and snails and puppy dog's tails,
That's what little boys are made of.

R Southey,
Oxford Dictionary of Nursery Rhymes 1951

Not true, but the nursery rhyme does reflect what everybody knows: there are differences between the sexes. Obvious and reasonably well understood in some cases such as biological differences; not so well understood in other areas such as psychological experiences of masculinity and femininity. Differences in health also exist. Men live shorter lives than women, patterns and prevalence of particular illnesses vary between the sexes. Opportunities to learn about health and acquire a health orientation also vary.

Women's health is more accessible. There is a Women's Health Council, a Rape Crisis Centre, a Well Woman Clinic, a Crisis Pregnancy Agency, a Women's Health Strategy and a plethora of women's magazines that have a focus on women's health.

You want information on men's health. Where do you turn to? Sources don't readily spring to mind. This is despite the fact that life expectancy for males in Ireland is approximately six years less than it is for females and men are more likely than females to die from cancer, heart disease, HIV infection, accidents and suicide. Men are more likely to drink more than the recommended alcohol limits, to be overweight, to use illegal drugs or to expose themselves to the sun without using sun cream. Men are more than twice as likely as women to have a major or minor accident and men are much less likely than women to consult a GP or dentist.

Despite these startling statistics there is no men's health council, men's health strategy or coordinated forum or response. A host of possible explanations exists to explain poor health status and a minimal or non-existent focus on this area. Reasons include a requirement to conform to a stereotypical male image of being in control, not wanting to appear weak, needy and unwell. Some men are unaware of the connections and some are just plain fearful, ignoring warning signs and putting off that trip to the doctor. Poor lifestyle behaviour, smoking, excess drinking, poor attention to diet and genetic influences also play a part.

A particularly difficult area is that of sexuality and relationships. Messages that come to boys about sex are confusing: schools and parents push abstention and restraint but lad's magazines, TV and soaps celebrate sexual license. In sex education classes, where they exist, sex is portrayed as an act, a set of mechanical aims and skills without any emotional content. Girls discuss and are given license to discuss the ramifications of the relationships they are involved in, stretching and developing their understanding of emotions, boys don't talk much about this, keeping their friends at bay and rarely discussing problems in their love life with male friends. As a result many men find it hard to form intimate relationships. Another area where men are poorly prepared is that of basic domestic sense. Girls learn domestic life skills from an early age but a natural work shyness in domestic circumstances may be stamped out in girls yet indulged in boys. These patterns persist through adult life with obvious consequences for health and well-being. Little research has been carried out to determine whether poorer morbidity and all those lost years of life represent an appalling inequality or an accident of birth, a consequence of genetic inheritance.

Despite the lack of research and information about the sociology and psychology of men's health there has been an increasing level of activity on the issue of men's health. Conferences have been held, reports have been written, there is a promise of a men's health policy in the south of Ireland, research projects are underway and pockets of activity exist throughout the island. I thought it would be useful to document what is going on. Find out what projects exist, collate information and make it available so that opinions and expertise can be shared. So this is what I have selected as my leadership project. I am taking a lead in collecting, compiling and disseminating this information. I have decided to do this because I believe that, despite common currency expressions like, 'it's a man's world', it is in fact quite tough being a man in the early part of the 21st Century.

Life expectancy and mortality figures represent stark statistics to compel focus, but other reasons such as changing work practices, increased participation and achievement by females in the workplace mean changing roles with implications for male status in the traditionally male dominated areas of upper management, power and privilege.

Parental expectations are also changing and Jenny Murray points out in her book 'That's my boy – A modern parent's guide to raising a happy and confident son' (1993) that expectant parents have a notion that boys are trouble with a capital 'T' whereas girls are desirable, the future, better behaved, higher academic achievers, more loyal to their parents as adults and easier to communicate with. The 'boy child' may no longer be the prized possession he once was. She also talks about parents who fail to pass on basic skills such as domestic responsibility and physical restraint to their male children as 'raising a man who will be a rod for some poor woman's back' and a home where a father never lifts a vacuum cleaner as having the potential to damn a son's future wife to a life of drudgery.

I want better health for all, but being a father, son and man I particularly want better health for men. Women take better care of their health than men and frequently they are the minders of men's health as well. It's time to realise that it is ok for men to take care of their own health and for an environment and ethos to develop which supports them in doing this. I consider it is now time to bring real focus to the area of men's health. Aspects of men's physical health are well understood but it is time to get a better understanding of the sociology and psychology of men's health. What are the determinants of men's health and what are those who are addressing men's health doing.

Documenting baseline activity is a start, but stemming from this there will be opportunities to bring the lead players together to ask what the issues are and how they might be responded to.

What the leadership programme contributes to my project.

Participating in this programme has convinced me that it is worthwhile exploring this area. Without the programme, ongoing passive interest would have characterised my level of commitment. So this more concrete engagement is a product of the programme.

The programme has encouraged participants to speak up for what they believe in. I believe that men's health can be improved at individual level and population level and that many factors combine to present us with the current startling situation.
I believe that this issue is not seen as important at a political level and that within the health services men's health is a second class citizen. Men are not encouraged to take care of their own health and there are few opportunities for them to learn more about their health. Gender studies and decent sex education and relationships education for all at school would be a good starting place. Doctor's surgeries – although presenting an opportunity for

men to unashamedly acknowledge their feminine side, in that they are allowed to look at women's magazines, simply because there is no choice – are not male friendly. I think we can do much better at informing, educating and encouraging men in ways that will increase their chances of having healthier lives. We can provide environments that are supportive of better health for men and we can promote greater access to health services for men.

This programme has challenged me to lead. It has given me opportunities to receive feedback that has strengthened my resolve. Psychological profiles, personality tests, feedback mechanisms, role play, simulation exercises have assisted understanding of what barriers may block us from making progress with our chosen leadership challenge and what strengths we can build on to help us push through and achieve stated leadership goals. The programme helped me understand that I am not alone in wanting change. This gives me strength. There are many areas to contribute for better health. Combined commitment to a range of issues will make a difference.

It is my hope that this work will add to an understanding of men's health issues and be a catalyst for action leading to longer healthier lives for men.

We Real Cool
The pool players
Seven at the Golden Shovel

We real cool. We
Left school. We

Lurk late. We
Strike straight. We

Sing sin. We
Thin gin. We

Jazz June. We
Die soon.

G Brooks in The Rag and Bone Shop of the Heart,
Poems for Men, 1992

Classification

Jane Wilde

'It's at the edges that interesting things happen.'

Estyn Evans, 1973
The Personality of Ireland

In Ireland we have our borders.
In public health it's the same.
We are always introducing new classifications:

The social model, the medical model

Population health, health promotion

Qualitative research, quantitative research

Epidemiology, social science

Multidisciplinary, unidisciplinary approaches

Physical health, mental health

Classification has value. It defines our interest and knowledge.
It allows us space to feel safe, a place to share our passions and
our prejudices. It offers us a chance to belong to a group.

But public health is not rooted in a particular model, method or profession.

Rather it is played out in multiple settings, in neighbourhoods, in communities, requiring contributions from people with a wide range of backgrounds, skills and experiences.

For those who cannot abide plurality and ambiguity the easiest way is to shore up the boundaries and resist questioning with a defensive pose.

Arundhati Roy writes of 'a team of trolls on their separate horizons patrolling the Blurry End'.

Think of a whole army of defenders marching up and down, assuming what others think and what others do.

Imagine if instead of retreating to the trenches and engaging in a smokescreen of rhetoric, the public health armies concentrated on fighting the wars that need to be fought:

> The war against injustice and poverty
>
> The war against unnecessary production and advertising of unhealthy foods
>
> The war against the multi-millionaire drugs barons
>
> The war against the mighty tobacco manufacturers
>
> The war to expose the dubious practices of some pharmaceutical companies

In public health, knowledge is our weapon. Boundaries separate us and if we keep shoring them up, fail to stretch over them and reach out, we stop learning, waste energy and resources and fail to change

Unnecessary dichotomies threaten to subvert our work.

We need to think of the imaginative possibility of a healthy society, with knowledge multiply situated. Those who work to create it need the capacity to negotiate boundaries and understand conflicting obligations.

In our minds as well as our meetings, we need to create places where we can discuss difference, describe beliefs and values, about meanings and engage in real conversation which acknowledges and respects each other. In the leadership programme we have reached out across the edges.

A risky business – what designing and delivering this programme has meant for me

Anne McMurray

Leadership development is a high risk business for programme designers and participants. You don't know when you start out where exactly it will end up. As someone who is involved in planning and running leadership development programmes, I find that the more I know about it, the more I have to learn. You might think this is surprising but I think it is important for me to be aware of this. It stops me from being complacent.

I believe there is no script or formula for leadership. We each do our 'leadership' in our unique character. This is true in the arena of leadership to build a healthy society in Ireland. What is required to undertake such a task is groundbreaking in its style and methods.

For me, the excitement of this programme has been to support a group of talented adults who are already leaders in their work domains, to try and take their effectiveness as leaders up a gear.

By the time these people had decided to join this leadership development programme, the 'low hanging fruit' had been taken care of. What I mean is they had already made the obvious or easy changes to develop themselves. This is because they are self aware and motivated to improve. They have probably been working on their self development most of their lives consciously or unconsciously.

Developing the leadership of someone who is already a leader means enabling them to make a more deep-rooted shift in how they operate. It is to do with building self confidence and personal mastery. It is not about 'putting in' knowledge and skills to address some deficit. It is about 'pulling out' latent potential and assisting the individual to take their next steps of growth as a human being.

Leadership development involves working with the whole person – with their intellect, stamina, emotion, will, values, relationships, their past as well as their future hopes and dreams. This means getting to the heart of how a person sees themselves and others. This may lead to challenging some of their necessary defence mechanisms, which we have all developed to help survive career and real life.

Leadership development can involve deconstructing a person's sense of themselves and others, destabilising how they see the world and encouraging them to let go of psychological handholds. This can make a person feel a heightened sense of vulnerability and reality. The development process lasts until they have been able to reconstruct all of the above in a new way.

The Centre for Creative Leadership who co-deliver the first event of the programme describes this as the ACS approach to leadership development: assessment, challenge and support. For an individual that means assessing the reality of my current approach and performance as a leader, being challenged to develop in areas where I could improve my effectiveness and securing the support I need from others to help me achieve this.

This happens at the level and pace the person chooses. As a designer of this process I see my job to be a guide and a helper; to try and make sure that any ground that has been taken away is put back under a person's feet before the process ends.

Designing and delivering leadership programmes should not, therefore, be undertaken lightly as a superficial exercise. It will dig as deep into the designer as it does the participants. This is necessary for the process to be experienced as real and authentic. It is not a 'doing to' – but a 'going with'.

Through the IPH programme I have developed some insights into my own experience of leading leadership development. This resonates with experiences from other programmes and people I have worked with. I am very grateful to have had the opportunity to be given the challenge of working with this programme and to the individuals who have taught me more than they will ever realise about leadership and me.

The main learning for me has been to do with managing myself, my feelings and emotions as I enjoin, albeit from a different angle, the experience that the group is going through.

First, usually leading/co-leading the delivery, I am aware that I may be sometimes the focus of the group's emotions. For example, if the group is uncertain of the task and the territory that is being explored, I may experience resistance and avoidance. Sometimes problems between group members may not be able to be addressed within the group and there might be an expectation placed upon me to sort it out. Or I am cast into a parental role, for example in regard to practical issues like being told the coffee's run out and can I sort it, as I am planning the next session. None of this is intended as negative – it is a result of the dynamics which inevitably occur in group life. The same sort of projections happen to anyone in a leadership role.

My challenge is to manage my emotions at these times and not become victim to my feelings. I need to keep thinking and understanding what is really happening, so as to come up with an intervention which can help things make progress. Keeping my ego out of the leadership development process is a number one priority. It is a big risk to my effectiveness if I don't contain it.

The second challenge is sorting out boundaries with the group, especially at the start of the process. The group and the individuals in the group need time to establish themselves in this new set of relationships. Individuals and the group itself need to define their own identity.

The group develops its own micro-culture and personality. Membership of the group is uniquely experienced by each person. Despite the strong temptation to enter and become part of this attractive system, I need to have distance and perspective. This comes from being some way apart. The group must perceive me as equally accessible to everyone.

Experience of the group process is hugely developmental. Much of an individual's growth is stimulated in relationship with the others. For this reason the private life of the group must be given space to unfold. People need to be together to reflect, gossip, joke, release pressure and form bonds outside of the formal agenda of the programme.

Non-attachment to popularity is essential for me to be able to handle this. My goal is to help develop the group into a supportive system and network. This has always been an explicit aim of the Institute's programme. To assist this process, I have to stand outside. It is hard to challenge a system on which I am emotionally dependent. This boundary can be let go of now the programme is ending and I look forward to entering relationships more freely and on equal terms with the individuals who have taken part in it.

The third challenge for me is to notice and regulate how my own behaviour fits with what I say. I have a very visible role. My credibility is weakened by incongruous or hypocritical behaviours or words. Rather than this being a pressure, it is the main prompt for me to put in place the space and support I need to examine my own development needs. In this way my leadership develops – by facing up to my personal growth challenges, so I can take on what I am encouraging others to do.

Based on my experience, I believe that leadership development can only occur in a benign and safe atmosphere which enables each individual, including myself, to surrender to the journey of development .

My colleague Mhairi Cameron has coined the phrase 'safely dangerous', which sums up for me what the aim of leadership development is about. Creating the safety for people to explore the dangerous excitement of finding out new potential in oneself as an adult, and realising there are always personal and relational frontiers to be explored in this life.

The falling point

Eleanor Gill

I'm standing at the top of the ladder – frozen, exposed, embarrassed.

Below me, many willing hands cupped together forming a safe and soft blanket to catch and cradle me. All I have to do is to allow myself to fall – let go. Accept their gift – give others the chance to help me – let them in.

I let go. The falling point brings the prize, the learning …

Trust

Growth

Strength

Security

Warmth

Release

I am not so afraid of my vulnerability now – I accept it and allow others to see it. I let myself fall more often and be supported. As a leader I know I don't have to have all the answers, I don't have to hide my weaknesses, I don't have to hold everything together on my own …

… good and caring people surround me ready to cup their hands to catch me whenever I fall.

My task now as a leader is to help others to reach their falling point, take the risk – and trust!

Trust in people: trusting people

Jane Wilde

She felt nervous and apprehensive as she was climbing the ladder.
She knew that hesitation would be fatal.

She climbed higher, tightening her grip.
Rising waves of panic.
She couldn't let go and what made it worse
was the knowing that everyone could see her fear.
She stood for ages.

It was always clear that we didn't have to do it.
Several chose not to.
She wanted to overcome her fear of heights.
She wanted to face her personal challenge.

Eventually she let go and fell backwards into a sea
of connected hands.

It's not easy to let go, particularly if you are scared of heights.
Asking for help can seem like a failure.

Afterwards, everyone said well done, you did it, you were great.
At the time she didn't feel that.
She felt embarrassed, and traumatised.

But she gave me a double gift.
She allowed me and others to help her.

More importantly, she demonstrated that leadership does not
mean always being invulnerable, able to do everything.

She showed me how to acknowledge the challenges I'm facing,
to say that I fear things, to ask for and receive help.

who we are

Ruth Barrington

I am Chief Executive of the Health Research Board. I participated in the Public Health Leadership course because it was the first multi-disciplinary, all-island development course for people concerned about public health.

Joe Barry

I am a citizen first and then a public health doctor and advocate for public health. I am currently senior lecturer in public health in Trinity College and specialist in public health medicine at the Eastern Regional Health Authority. I joined the public health leadership programme because I believe in its founding principles. I am very privileged to be part of the network that has been created and hope that the vision that led to its creation is realised.

Gillie Bolton

I am a Senior research fellow in medicine and the arts at King's College London, and reflective writing consultant to the leadership programme. I have published three books and many papers, and am associate editor to two medical journals.

Leslie Boydell

I am the Programme Director for the leadership programme and Associate Director of the Institute of Public Health in Ireland. Having created this programme, I have been involved in every aspect of development and delivery and have found it a privilege to be part of this process with this group of leaders.

John Briggs

I am currently Strategic Director with Armagh City and District Council with responsibility for environment, health and recreation issues. My professional qualifications are in Environmental Health, including acoustics and air pollution control. I believe my current role allows me to promote the influence of environment and lifestyle factors on personal and community health.

Sean Denyer

I am currently the Director of the Programme of Action for Children for the Health Board Executive. I have got a huge amount out of the leadership programme, new skills, new friends and a new determination to improve the health of people in Ireland.

Cecilia Forrestal

I am a community development worker with Community Action Network. I joined the leadership programme because I believe that community development has a significant contribution to make to a healthy Ireland. I learned that honest dialogue plays a key role in creating new insights across difference.

Eleanor Gill

I'm the Chief Executive of the General Consumer Council of Northern Ireland. Previously I led the Armagh and Dungannon Health Action Zone which promotes a community partnership approach to health. I am privileged to have been a part of this all-island programme. Above all it has given us the opportunity to focus on the importance of leadership and connection across all sectors in making life better for everyone out there.

Catherine Hazlett

I am a Principal Officer in the Department of Social and
Family Affairs. I work in the Business Development Division
of the Department with responsibility for E-Government,
E-Services and the development of the strategic direction
of the Department's business.

Elizabeth Keane

I was appointed first Director of Public Health to
the Southern Health Board in Spring 1995. I chose to
participate in the public health leadership programme to
enhance skills and competencies required to lead a vibrant
public health function, and to broaden my horizon and
networks to make for a healthier society.

Carolyn Mason

I work as one of the four Nursing Officers at the Department
of Health, Social Services and Public Safety. I found the
idea of learning and exploring with others from different
backgrounds really exciting. The programme has had a huge
impact on me – creativity is the source of a lot of our best
work, and when we all pull our different areas and
organisations together for public health, it works.

John McMullan

I am Executive Director of Bryson House, one of Northern
Ireland's oldest (Est.1906) and largest NGOs, focused on
developing and demonstrating innovative approaches to new
and emerging social need. My participation in the
leadership programme has enabled me through self-
assessment, coaching and learning to both understand and
develop my leadership potential.

Anne McMurray

I have worked as an organisation development consultant since 1989. I combine a systems approach to organisation development with developing individual leadership at all levels. As programme consultant I have worked closely with the Institute of Public Health since 2000 to design and deliver the programme, which has been a highly developmental and enjoyable experience.

Karen Meehan

I have worked with Derry Well Woman since 1989, initially as co-ordinator, and since 2000 as manager of a project to develop a cross border health strategy for women in the North West. The strategy Other Borders was produced in June 2003. I am now overseeing its implementation. The leadership programme has introduced me to people, ideas and parts of myself that have made my work richer.

Owen Metcalfe

I am Associate Director of the Institute of Public Health in Ireland. The leadership programme is a great opportunity to learn, to get to know others and appreciate the real talent for leadership for public health that exists on the island.

Ivan Perry

I am Professor of Public Health and Head of Department of Epidemiology and Public Health, University College Cork. I joined the programme to help focus my work and that of our academic department on research and teaching that supports the public health agenda in Ireland. I have thoroughly enjoyed the programme and have learned a lot about leadership, public health and myself over the past two years.

Ruth Sutherland

I am committed to working for social justice, which is at the heart of how health for all can be reached. I am the Director of the Community Development and Health Network, an NGO based in Northern Ireland. I have been keen to participate in the public health leadership programme and network to learn, grow and contribute to an all-Ireland public health movement.

Anne Marie Telford

I am the Director of Public Health of the Southern Health and Social Services Board based in Armagh, and the Board's lead Director for our Investing for Health Partnership and Health Action Zone. The programme has provided a wonderful opportunity to learn, to develop and to form a strong alliance with others working for a healthier society.

Helen Whelton

I am Senior Lecturer in Dental Public Health and Preventive Dentistry and Director of the Oral Health Services Research Centre, University College Cork. The leadership programme has extended my professional network and broadened my horizons.

Jane Wilde

I'm committed to the idea of a strong multi-disciplinary public health movement across the island. As Director of the Institute of Public Health and a programme participant I am full of admiration and gratitude to fellow participants and all who are helping to realise this vision.